Keeping Honeybees

P

G000041590

Contents

Introduction

Beekeeping is an occupation which can easily become an obsession. The fascination is in part due to the way they function as a social unit : each bee is integral to the collective whole with clearly defined roles performed at set times and the general survival of the colony coming before the well-being of any individual member. Since honeybees evolved from wasp-like ancestors as much as 150 million years ago—shortly after the appearance of the first flowering plants—their habits are thought to have greatly influenced the evolution of flowers into the forms we know today. Another attraction is that keeping bees keeps you in touch with nature. Their dependence on weather conditions and which flowers are in bloom make one very aware of

the seasons, the rain and sun, and whether there is a good dandelion crop that year—in fact everyday occurrences that can sometimes pass one by in the hurry to proceed with life. And last but not least of the enjoyments is the deliciousness of honey—the bonus of beekeeping and also the prize for having successfully looked after and managed the hive throughout the year.

Beekeeping is an ancient craft, its date of origin unknown. The earliest evidence of man taking honey is recorded in a neolithic rock-painting in the Cuevas de la Arana in Valencia which shows two men climbing ropes to a small hole in a cliff to collect honey from a swarm of bees. The habit of keeping bees in skeps or other hollow receptacles probably began with the Ancient Egyptians in about the third century BC and continued unchanged

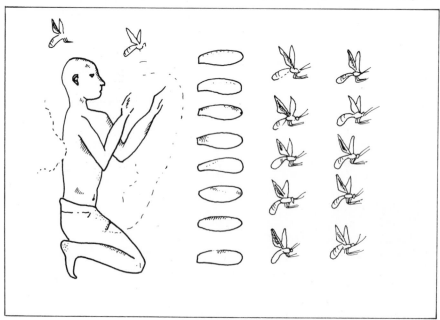

until the end of the nineteenth century. At about this time a number of technical advances were made, among them the invention of the modern hive, movable frames, the metal smoker, honey extractors and mass-produced glass jars for marketing, all of which moved beekeeping in a few quick steps from the dark ages into the twentieth century. However, they were advances which changed the art of beekeeping rather than the bees, who stalwartly stick to their ancient instincts and habits whatever modern science superimposes. Because bees are such instinctive creatures it is really only through practical experience that one can properly learn about them. A book can introduce the subject and provide some basic rules, but the rest must come from watching and handling them personally. In this short book I have tried to set out the basic steps,

but I whole-heartedly advise anyone wishing to keep bees to have a practical demonstration before attempting to go it alone. Local bee associations and the large bee appliance manufacturers, often run courses as so do some agricultural colleges but, failing this, try and find a friend who will help to teach you. Everyone will be very friendly ; beekeepers are, generally speaking, nice people, probably due to the sensitivity of bees which will not tolerate the arrogant, the impatient, the immoral or thrive where there is strife in a household. Handling someone else's bees will also show whether you are temperamentally suited to keeping bees or allergic to bee-stings before you embark on the trouble and expense of acquiring a hive. First begin with one and build from there as you gain experience and confidence. Bees are surprisingly trouble-free. Unlike other creatures, they can generally be left alone to look after themselves. There are many who keep bees with reasonable success, only opening the hive twice a year : once in the spring to have a general inspection and to attach supers, then again in the autumn to remove the honey, leaving the rest to chance. However, more frequent attention will be a greater guarantee of success, as I hope the following pages will explain.

(*opposite page*) Detail from Ancient Egyptian tomb

Siting the Hive

The ideal site for a hive is sheltered, facing south to south-east and within easy reach of good feeding. Depending on the circumstances, however, other factors will probably have to be taken into consideration. While aiming for a site which has maximum advantage for the bees so that the production of honey can continue unabated, the social and practical implications of keeping bees must also be taken into account.

Bees fly in a slowly rising straight line from their hive to their immediate source of food and, if this is across a road or someone else's garden, there is the possibility of collision and consequent stinging. Therefore, if bees are kept in heavily populated surroundings, a hedge or fence about 1.8m (6ft) high and placed about 2.4m (8ft) from the hive will force the bees to rise up immediately after leaving the hive in order to fly over the hedge and so prevent any accidents.

If you are going to keep several hives in one place, make sure that there is sufficient room to keep them 91–121cm (3–4ft) apart in every direction. This enables each to be looked after without the other hives being disturbed. Not more than thirty hives should be kept on one site and, ideally, these should be arranged in a semi-circle so that the angle of approach is different for each bee. With a prevailing wind, if the hives are in a line, drifting down the line will occur eventually making the population in the bottom hive greater than the one at the top.

Hives should be placed on a firm stand, clear of the ground. Suitable plinths can be made using bricks, breeze

Hive on breeze blocks

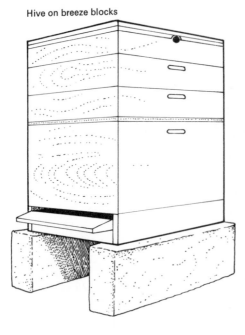

blocks or concrete. National hives are often placed on planks of wood laid on bricks ; this makes transportation easier. The wooden legs of WBC hives should stand on stones or bricks in order to prevent them from rotting. Keep the surrounding vegetation short, as grass growing in front of the entrance will impede the bees' flight path and grass growing too long under the hive will make it damp. Hives should slope downwards towards the front so that any damp can drain out of the entrance. This can be achieved by using small pieces of slate to prop up the back.

While hives should be protected from strong winds since they can blow over, they should not be overhung or placed in a frost pocket. The object is to keep the air around the hive still but not damp and unnecessarily cold. Hives standing in fields with stock in them should be protected by a fence as animals can come along and knock them over.

Hives facing south-east will have an advantage over those placed in other directions. Bees rise with the sun and the sooner this reaches the entrance of the hive, the sooner they will be out beginning the day's foraging.

A final consideration in siting a hive is the source of food. The average area of country, garden suburb or town will produce an adequate supply of blossoms to support up to thirty hives. For anything above this amount an increasingly scientific and specialized approach will have to be adopted, and hives may have to be transported to their food source. Of these the most common sources are large fruit orchards in spring. A fruit farmer will

probably welcome you and may even pay a fee for the pollination work your bees will perform on his blossoms. Other sources of food in summer are fields of clover, bean and rape, and in the autumn heather moors. Because heather is a late crop, many small beekeepers, after removing the main honey crop in August, transport their stock to nearby moors for the bees to work the heather. This, depending on the area, is in bloom from late July until September.

Choice of Hive

Bees in the wild live in hollow trees, filling up the space with wax combs, in which each cell is used to house eggs, pollen and nectar. Hives are designed to reproduce these conditions but with improvements.

In primitive parts of the world, bees are still kept in holes in trees or hollowed out tree stumps placed upside down. Tolstoy, in *Anna Karenina*, describes Levin keeping bees in hollow stumps. In Britain, however, they were always kept in skeps, often placed in special bee houses, or in niches in stone walls. A skep was made from ropes of straw bound with willow bands in the shape of a waste-paper basket and then mounted on a wooden hoop with a hole cut for the entrance. Skeps are still sold but their contemporary use is for collecting swarms. This is a wasteful way of beekeeping because of the fixed combs since it meant that, in order to take the honey, the whole colony had to be killed and all the combs destroyed. The methods by which bees were destroyed were either puffing sulphur smoke into the hive or holding the whole skep over a pit of burning sulphur; the combs were then cut out and the honey extracted under pressure. Since only the heaviest skeps were selected each autumn, the newly swarmed and lighter ones being left to provide the next year's supply, it frequently meant that the strongest and most prolific bees were killed, leading to a gradual degeneration of the stock.

The modern, easily opened, weatherproof hives with movable combs and wax foundation release the bees at crucial times for foraging rather than for maintenance. The invention of the metal smoker has meant that the bees can, to some extent, be controlled and subjugated when the hive is opened, and the honey extractor allows for the production of liquid honey without the total destruction of the combs. All of these were nineteenth-century advances which have transformed beekeeping from a cottage activity into the commercial enterprise it is for some today.

There are five basic designs of modern hive which vary in popularity. The WBC and National are the most favoured in England, and the Smith in Scotland. The Langstroth and Modified Dadant which are larger, usually need two men to lift them, and are only really used by commercial beekeepers. Any of these may be bought new, fully constructed for an approximate outlay of £60; or, for

Skep

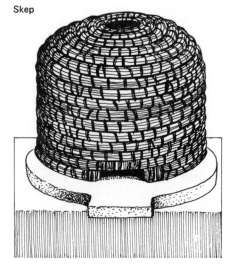

slightly less, you can buy a kit and construct it yourself. If you are adept, cost can be further reduced by making your own hive. Free leaflets with written instructions for building a National 367, Smith 445, Modified Commercial 468, Langstroth and Modified Dadant 549 are available from the Ministry of Agriculture, Fisheries and Food.

If you are starting to keep bees for the first time, it will be cheaper and more sensible to begin with a second-hand hive. Your local bee association will probably know of anyone in the area who has one for sale ; alternatively, look for advertisements in the local paper or bee magazines. If later, having gained experience, you decide to change your design of hive, you will not feel deterred by the money outlayed on the first. The only disadvantage of buying second-hand hives is that they are sometimes home-made to unorthodox measurements and can be infected with diseases. Make sure that you buy one of standard measurements, that the parts are well fitting and that the former occupants did not die from disease. Whatever the case may be, start with fresh wax foundation and scrub all the parts with hot water and soda. As an extra precaution against infection, run a blow-lamp over the inside as this is the only effective method of destroying the worst diseases such as American and European foulbrood.

All hives should be built of a light, well seasoned and sound material. Yellow deal is an old favourite but Canadian red cedar has gained popularity being light, durable and

requiring no treatment to keep it weatherproof. Other woods require a coating of creosote and paint. Recent experiments with hives made of synthetic fibre have proved unsuccessful since they are too light and tend to retain moisture.

WBC hive

National hive

Hives

WBC

Named after its designer, W. B. Carr, it is the most picturesque of the hives but, with an outer case around the inner parts, it is rather unwieldy. Because of its two walls which require more handling than other hives, it disturbs the bees and is also bulky to transport. In winter the two walls can become an advantage as they keep the brood chamber drier than in the other varieties. It holds ten frames measuring 35.5×21.5cm ($14 \times 8\frac{1}{2}$in).

National Hive

The commonest form of hive in Britain today, each storey is a complete square and is interchangeable. It holds eleven frames measuring 35.5×21.5cm ($14 \times 8\frac{1}{2}$in) and is easily manipulated and transported. As with all British standard hives its disadvantage is that the brood chamber often becomes too small and a second chamber or super has to be added to make more space ; another drawback is the floor, which has an insufficient gradient that tends to hold heavy rain.

Smith

Named after its designer, it is a popular hive in Scotland and a modification of the National. It uses British Standard frames with American shortened lugs, making it necessary to cut British Standard comb lugs to the 1.4cm ($\frac{9}{16}$in) required.

Modified Dadant

Popular with commercial beekeepers, it takes the largest frames of all, eleven measuring 45×28.5cm ($17\frac{5}{8} \times 11\frac{1}{4}$in) but also requires an especially large extractor.

Parts of the Hive

Floor

A shallow tray with an entrance.

Brood Box

A square frame of the right dimensions in which frames of comb are hung from lugs spaced 64–96cm ($\frac{1}{4}$–$\frac{3}{8}$in) apart. The queen lives and lays her eggs in the brood box.

Queen Excluder

A metal grille (ideally one on a wooden frame as others bend and get stuck down) with spaces large enough to allow the workers to pass through but too small for the queen to do so. Although they are used by the majority, opinions vary on the use of excluders, and some beekeepers will have nothing to do with them.

Supers

These are similar in construction to the brood box but shallower, holding frames with wax foundation in which surplus honey is stored. As the summer progresses and supers are filled, more are added to provide extra storage space.

Crownboard or Inner Cover

Fits over the top super, usually made of perforated zinc with a central hole over which the feeder or bee escape is placed.

Roof

Wood, covered with metal or roofing felt and preferably with a ventilator hole.

Frames

Each brood box and super is hung with frames which lie parallel to each other. Brood frames are deeper than the super frames (though sometimes brood-sized frames are used as supers and sometimes shallow super frames are used to enlarge the brood space). All must be exactly spaced; called a bee space the optimum is between 3.5–3.8cm ($1\frac{3}{8}$–$1\frac{1}{2}$in). If it is more, the bees will fill up the extra with wax; if less, they glue it together. Frames are made with lugs from which they hang and which rest on the grooved inner side of the hive. The width of the lug ensures that the mean bee space is maintained. In America they use the Hoffman spacing system with the upper third of short lugs broadened, but in England the less efficient system of fitting metal ends on to longer, wedge-shaped lugs is used. Each frame is fitted with a wax foundation imprinted with cells and, in the case of brood frames, strengthened with wire. The bees pull out the wax into cells.

Frames can be bought in kit form or ready-made. For comb honey, super frames are fitted with special wooden sections.

Division Board

A solid division board is useful to close up part of the brood chamber when some frames need to be separated from others, or when the full quota of frames is not being used.

1 Roof; 2 Crownboard; 3 Super; 4 Queen excluder; 5 Brood box; 6 Floor; 7 Entrance block

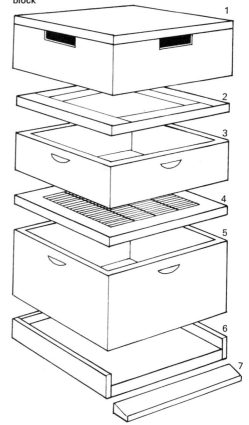

Everyday Equipment for the Maintenance of the Hive

Smoker

The most ancient and the most vital of the beekeeper's tools is smoke. This subdues the bees and makes their manipulation easier as well as reducing the likelihood of being stung. Originally, smouldering fabric or wood was used for smoke. A modern smoker consists of a firebox with bellows attached, the best kind being one with a bent nose and a reasonable sized firebox made of copper. This is infinitely superior to the small straight-nosed variety and as it is more durable and effective, it also stays alight longer, an important point for the beginner. Binder twine, sacking, corrugated paper or oily cotton rags can all be used as fuel. Light some and stuff it half-way down the firebox, puff the bellows to get it going well, then push the fuel right down, add some more and close the box. Continue working the bellows until it is going well and a good supply of smoke is rising from the nozzle.

Metal smoker

Control of the bees can be lost if a smoker fails to respond immediately at a critical point. Kept upright, a smoker should stay alight ; laid flat, it will go out. To extinguish it, plug the nozzle with some grass and lay it on its side. Clean well before using again.

Hive Tool

Bees stick everything down with propolis (bee-glue collected from trees and certain plants) and a hive tool is essential to prise off covers, supers, and to loosen the frames. It can also act as a scraper to clean covers and hive interiors. Made of steel it has a flat blade at one end—the prising end—and a bent one at the other for scraping.

Manipulating Cloths

These are useful to cover the part of an open hive not being examined, to keep the bees quieter and, on a cold morning, warmer. If something has been forgotten and needs fetching during examination, a manipulating cloth can also act as a temporary cover. Hessian sacks or dish-cloths will do but a length of canvas is the best material to use, with each end tacked to a wooden lathe so that the cloth can be rolled and unrolled as required.

Brush

A bee-brush is necessary to brush bees off combs or a fence during swarming. Traditionally, a goose feather is used though special bee-brushes can be bought.

Feeder

A late spring, prolonged bad weather in the summer or lack of supplies in autumn mean that the bees must be fed with sugar syrup to ensure their survival. There are several designs of feeder on the market, the two commonest being a polythene contact feeder, and a lacquer metal feeder. Both are placed over the hole in the cover board. With the polythene feeder the bees suck the syrup from the perforations in the top, which entails a slower and more gradual supply of food. With the metal feeder the bees crawl up the central hole and remove the syrup as quickly as they like, making it easier to give quick injections of feed. It is also possible to make a feeder yourself, either by covering glass jars with muslin or puncturing holes in the top of jam-jars, tins or polythene buckets.

A general-purpose sugar syrup is made by slowly heating 2.2kg (5lb) sugar in 1.1l (1qt) water until it is dissolved. When cool, the syrup is poured into the feeder and given to the bees, preferably in the evening.

Tool Box

A tool box is worth having since it keeps all the equipment together, facilitates transport and can be used as a store for spare fuel, notebook, and anything else that might be required.

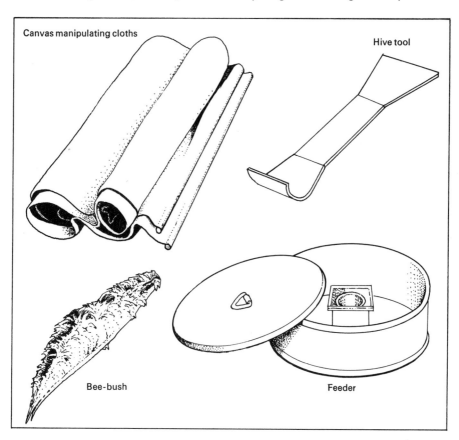

Canvas manipulating cloths

Hive tool

Bee-bush

Feeder

Clothing

The amount of protective clothing to be worn while handling bees is a debatable subject. The professional usually makes a minimal concession to the bees by wearing just a hat and veil. The amateur prefers to wear protective clothing and is advised to do so. The beginner has a greater tendency to make jarring movements and slight errors which will stimulate the sensitive bees, and cause them to rush out of the hive ready to sting in defence. Later on, when fully conversant with beekeeping, sureness of movement coupled with knowledge and experience will make this less likely to happen. Some bees, however, are inherently irritable so that even the experienced will have trouble dealing with them and have to wear full protective clothing.

Bees are without a strong sense of colour. They register brightness of colour rather than the colour itself, and can almost certainly only recognize four : yellow, blue-green, blue and ultra violet. They prefer pale coloured

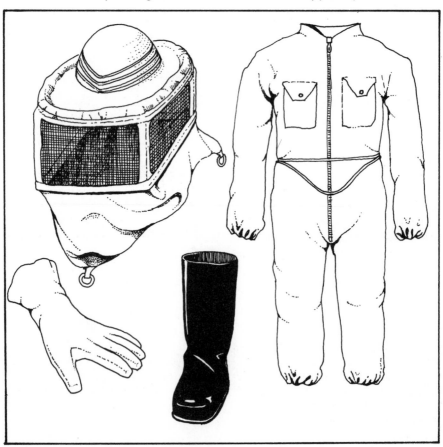

clothing to dark, and smooth rather than fuzzy clothes. White or pale-coloured cotton clothes are therefore preferable to dark-coloured wools. Bees always climb up, never down, and gaps should be closed with this in mind. The following are the correct clothes to wear. They can all be made at home or bought from an appliance manufacturer.

Hat and Veil

This can consist either of a cotton hat with a stiffened brim to which netting is attached, or a stiff hat with a veil mounted on a wire framework. The latter is best. A net veil can blow into the face enabling bees to sting around the eyes, nose and mouth, which is extremely painful. However, a stiff veil prevents this although its disadvantage is that it can be stuffy and heavy on a hot day.

Gloves

Being a coward, I always wear gloves though the experts seldom do since you can be more gentle without them. When you do wear gloves they should be of a supple leather with gauntlets. Thin rubber gloves are occasionally worn by people but whichever you choose, the gap between glove and sleeve should be tightly covered by a cuff and/or an elasticated gauntlet.

Overgarment

By far the best and easiest thing to wear is a white, zipped bee-suit. It covers all and is easy to put on. When buying, choose one made of cotton not nylon since this seems to upset the bees, probably due to the static electricity generated by friction. If you don't want

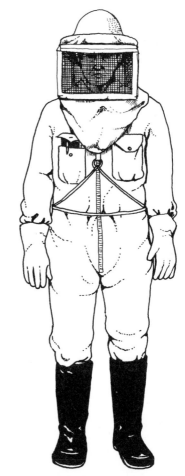

to go to this expense, jeans and a tough cotton shirt will be quite adequate. However, as stated, neither should be of too dark a colour. Make sure the shirt doesn't have gaps the bees can crawl through and wear it tucked into the trousers.

Shoes

Since bees crawl upwards, trousers should never be left hanging loose at the bottom but should be tucked into thick socks. The design of shoe is immaterial; you can wear leather boots, rubber gum-boots or thick shoes.

Acquiring Bees

The ideal strain of bee is good tempered, easy to handle, disease-free, disinclined to swarm and has good foraging qualities. Needless to say, this ideal bee has not yet been bred. However, these are the qualities which should be looked for and bees should be obtained from a source which meets these requirements as far as possible. It is also an advantage to acquire local bees. Strains become adapted to local conditions and a bee which works well in Somerset might not do so in another region such as London.

Bees can be acquired as a swarm from a neighbour or bought as a nucleus either through your local bee association or from a reputable dealer. If the bees are bought as a nucleus, the beginner will be well advised to start in spring with a four to six comb nucleus, headed by a young queen. This amount of bees is easily managed and the uninitiated will gain experience and confidence through handling and developing such a small number into a full-sized colony. Given a good season, you may even obtain some honey in the first year. A greater number of bees than this can be a daunting task and the temptation to begin with a full-sized, ten-frame colony in the hope of getting honey your first season should be avoided. The possibility of having honey will be much reduced by inexperienced management and the chance of swarms, added to which they will cost considerably more. Packages of bees with a caged queen, which are in effect swarms, have been for sale in recent years but these are only recommended for established beekeepers for the replenishment or increase of stocks. They need careful management and feeding in their early stages if they are to do well.

If the bees come as a swarm from a neighbour, try to ensure that it is a good, late May swarm. Hive them on frames of foundation and feed them for a while until they get going then, given a good season, they should produce a surplus of honey at the end of the year. This is the most satisfactory way to begin beekeeping. Unfortunately, however, swarms seldom arrive at the right time.

To hive a swarm, follow the instructions on p 38. To hive a nucleus follow these instructions:

1 The nucleus will arrive in a special travelling box of the correct size for the number of combs fitted with wire gauze panels for ventilation and a covered flight entrance; on arrival, this box should be placed beside the hive the bees will eventually inhabit. Uncover the entrance and allow the bees to fly for an hour or two before hiving. This gives them a chance to settle down.

2 If the time is not convenient or the weather inclement, cover the box to keep out the rain and leave it until conditions are suitable. The middle of a dry, warm day is best. Light your smoker and see that it is going properly. Dress yourself up in suitable clothing. Remove the screws in the top of the box. Puff a little smoke through the perforations and entrance and leave for a couple of minutes. Then gently remove the lid and, starting at one end, one by

Transferring combs

one transfer the combs into the hive, making sure that they are kept in the same order and the same distance apart that they were in the travelling box.

3 As each comb is lifted out by the lugs, it should be inspected. The requirements of the British Standard Specification BSS 1372 of 1947 for sold bees are that there should be : no visible signs of disease ; a laying queen and a worker brood in all stages covering at least half the comb area ; an average of 570g (1¼lb) honey and pollen per comb, and sufficient bees to fully cover all the combs. These specifications should be distributed throughout the combs as follows : the outside combs should have honey ; the inside ones capped brood, pale yellow-brown in colour ; uncapped cells with eggs and grubs in various stages of growth, and an outer ring of honey cells. The queen will probably be invisible, but, if there are worker eggs present, she is in all likelihood there.

4 After the combs have been transferred and you have checked that the queen is not in the bottom of the box—if she is, she should be coaxed on to the combs in the hive— shake all the remaining bees into one side of the box with a jerk and, turning the box over, shake them into the hive. Add a frame of foundation on either side of the end frames, close up the space with a dummy board, put on coverboard and roof and leave undisturbed for seven days. After this time, they should be inspected and a full complement of combs given.

If there is adequate honey in the combs, and the weather is fine, feeding should not be necessary. If not, however, syrup should be given and continued until conditions have improved with the foundation drawn out and the brood nest developing satisfactorily.

Functions of Bees and their Life Cycle

A colony builds up its strength slowly, throughout the year, until, towards the end of May or in early June, it reaches its maximum strength. This maximum is maintained for some time until the late summer and autumn when it gradually declines again, reaching its lowest level in mid-winter. A hive at full strength in summer can contain between 20,000 and 80,000 worker bees, a few hundred drones and a queen, together with combs containing brood in all stages of development, stores of honey and pollen.

Worker Bees

The Queen begins laying fertilized eggs in January. Fed by house bees on royal jelly, these tiny grubs or larvae grow rapidly and reach their full size within five days. Their cells are then sealed with porous wax cappings. The larvae turn into pupae and emerge as worker bees in twelve to fourteen days by chewing their way through the cappings. During the first few days of her life, the adult worker bee eats a large quantity of pollen which she obtains from storage cells. By the time she is twelve days old, she is ready to begin work as a house bee building and repairing comb and, if weather conditions permit, makes a series of play or orientation flights during which she learns to place her hive and its surroundings. Between twelve and twenty-one days the average worker bee performs the duty of relieving the incoming foragers of their loads of pollen and nectar. They also convert the nectar into honey, storing away both it and the pollen in cells. At the same time, she does a lot of house-cleaning such as carrying out dead bees and debris. At twenty-one days she takes up foraging duties : collecting water, nectar, pollen and sometimes propolis. This she continues to do until from exhaustion and old age, she dies some two to three weeks later at the height of the season. At other times of the year, when work is less arduous, she lives far longer and those born in autumn survive the winter.

Worker

Drone Bees

Drone eggs are laid by the queen from March onwards, in the larger cells found in the combs on the outer edges of the brood nest. After nine to ten days the eggs have grown into larvae and are sealed with the distinctive domed caps. They emerge as adult drone bees fifteen days later. Drones are burly, squarish bees with large eyes and no sting. Their main function in the hive is to impregnate the queen. A drone comes from an unfertilized egg so has genes only from its mother. Sexually mature when ten to fourteen days old, they live for four to five weeks in summer, congregating in the warmest part of the hive, fortuitously helping incubate brood but performing no other duties apart from fertilizing the queen. This chance happens to few drones but, on the other hand, with so many drones, the likelihood of the queen not finding a mate is so small that the continuance of the colony is ensured.

At the end of the summer, their time of possible usefulness over, drones are starved of food by the other bees. They drop to the bottom of the hive to be pulled outside to die of exposure. If there are still drones present in the hive at the end of summer, it is an indication that something is wrong.

because, by secreting a substance called queen substance, she provides a cohesive force which keeps the colony together as a social unit. Queen cells are erected by workers in a free, hanging position often on the edges of comb and are used only once. Ordinary worker eggs are laid and it is through special feeding of royal jelly that a queen is developed. She spends eight days as a larvae before being capped, to emerge as a queen seven days later. She is then a larger and longer bee than a worker, with no equipment for

Drone

Queen

It is thought that there are special meeting places of drones to which virgin queens are attracted on their mating flight. This would explain why it is impossible to selectively mate queens. Mating takes place in flight, the drone grabbing the queen and inserting his genitalia so tightly that the queen can only break away by rupturing the drone and tearing him in half, resulting in the death of the drone. Having broken free, the queen returns to her hive with the mating sign, the remains of the drone's genitalia, protruding from her vagina.

Queen

Without a mated queen, no colony can survive. This is due partly to her reproductive function and partly

collecting or processing food, and with a sting which she only uses against other queens, killing off any rivals within one or two days of emerging from her cell. At this time, too, she helps herself to food and makes a number of short orientation flights. Her mating flight is made about ten days after hatching, usually between noon and four in the afternoon on a fine day. Within three or four days of mating, she begins wandering around laying eggs within the brood area in any unoccupied cell. The sperm she receives from the drone lasts her lifetime, enabling her to fertilize several hundred-thousand worker eggs.

A queen normally lives and heads her colony for two to three years.

Bees' Food: Pollen and Honey

Pollen

Pollen provides the protein in a bee's diet that is necessary for the development of the larvae and for the full development of young adult bees. Lack of it can lead to paralysis. There should be adequate supplies stored in the hive at all times and sufficient reserves for the winter (at least four British Standard brood combs) so that brood reared during February can be fed and the colony given a good start for the season. Bewteen 22.7 and 45.3kg (50 and 100lb) pollen per hive are consumed in a season representing between 2 to 4 million bee-loads. The precise way in which bees gather pollen varies according to the structure of the flower concerned. When collecting from flowers such as dandelions and roses, the bee moves quickly about the stamens often gathering them together with her legs and biting at them with her mandibles to dislodge the pollen grains. Then, hovering in the air, she gathers together the pollen grains adhering to her body hairs, mixes them into a paste with nectar or regurgitated honey and packs them into the pollen baskets situated on the back legs for transport back to the hive. There they can be clearly seen as bright bundles of colour—yellow, orange, green, etc—showing the flower source of the pollen.

Nectar

This supplies the carbohydrate in the diet of both larvae and adult bees in addition to providing them with the majority of their water. Nectar is composed from traces of salts, acids, enzymes, protein and aromatic substances together with three predominating sugars, glucose, fructose and sucrose. In the process of converting nectar into honey, most of the sucrose is broken down into the simpler sugars of glucose and fructose by the addition by the bees of the enzyme invertase, while the average water content of 60 per cent is reduced to 20 per cent. This is brought about in the following way : on returning to the hive with a load of nectar, the forager gives most of it to a household bee who seeks out a quiet place and manipulates the nectar with her tongue, regurgitating it from her honey stomach perhaps eighty to ninety times during the course of about twenty minutes, reducing the water content by about 15 per cent. She then deposits it in a cell—one that is empty or one already containing some semi-processed nectar—and eventually, after perhaps more manipulation and exposure to the warm air of the hive which further reduces the water content, the cell is sealed.

Each plant secretes its own kind of nectar from special organs called nectaries, so producing its own typical honey. Few honeys are totally pure, most consist of a mixture of nectars from various plants usually with one predominant nectar. The concentration of sugars in the different nectars varies enormously. Some are quite dilute while others, such as pear and lime are highly concentrated. However, this concentration can vary from day to day and even from hour to hour, depending on the weather, the

temperature and the altitude. Too much moisture in the air or soil dilutes the nectar reducing its value and attraction to the bees. Cool nights followed by warm days are said to help nectar secretion by clover plants, but the optimum day temperature varies from plant to plant and is lower for spring-blooming flowers than for those of mid-summer, when the ideal is 26–29°C (80–85°F). Heather growing at sea-level produces little nectar compared with heather at 300m (1000ft) or more.

The main nectar crops of the year are as follows :

Spring

Cherry, pear, apple, currant, gooseberry, maple, sycamore, hawthorn, dandelion, cabbage

Early Summer

Raspberry, field beans, white clover, lucerne

Summer

Lime, red clover, sainfoin, willow herb, brambles, heather

Garden plants especially favoured by bees are : anchusa, arabis, aubretia, borage, berberis, buckthorn, buddleia, campanula, canterbury bells, crane's bill, centaurea, cornflower, clarkia, cotoneaster, crocus, catmint, dahlia, forget-me-not, fuchsia, gilia, honeysuckle, heliotrope, linaria, limnanthes, mignonette, mallow, michaelmas daisy, narcissus, phacelia, poppy, salvia, sedum, scabious, snowdrop, thistle, verbascum, veronica, wall-flower.

Bee Diseases

Bee diseases fall into two categories : those which attack the brood and those which attack the adult bees. Signs of the latter are large numbers of dead bees, bees crawling about unable to fly outside the hive or a large decrease in the number of foragers. The former are only spotted by detailed inspection of the brood combs and even then the amateur may find it difficult, particularly when the combs are darkened with age and use. Signs to look for are dead larvae in cells, a patchy brood pattern and cappings which are sunken, dark or perforated. If these suspicious signs are present, contact your local beekeeping association for advice. Many county councils employ a special beekeeping officer while others rely on an established beekeeper to give advice. The address of whichever one is closest to you can be otained by looking in the Yellow Pages under Government Departments, Local Offices. Where neither is available, a sample comb showing the signs of the diseases, preferably one containing brood in all stages of development but without much honey, wrapped in several layers of newspaper with a covering letter inside the wrappings, but not against the comb, should be sent to : The Beekeeping Adviser, Agricultural Development and Advisory Service, Rothamsted Lodge, Hatching Green, Harpenden, Hertfordshire. If you live in Wales you should send them to : The Beekeeping Adviser, Agricultural Development and Advisory Service, Trawscoed, Aberystwyth, Dyfed.

For diseases of adult bees, a sample of not less than thirty bees all from the same hive in a clearly labelled matchbox should be sent to the same address.

The law stipulates that all colonies of bees must be inspected by a local official at least once every three years, though most do it every year. If disease is present, he will do whatever is necessary. In the case of American and European foulbrood, having reported it to the authorities, it is usually necessary to destroy all the bees and combs. Then the hive must be thoroughly disinfected. Scrape off, collect and burn the brace comb or propolis and scorch the interior of the hive, including all separate parts, with a blow-lamp, taking care that no cracks and corners are overlooked. Appliances such as the queen excluder, smoker and hive tool, which you are unable to treat with the lamp, should be thoroughly scrubbed with a brush dipped in the following solution : 450g (1lb) washing soda dissolved in 4.5l (1gal) hot water, with 25g ($\frac{1}{2}$lb) chloride lime added. Stir and leave for the sediment to settle. Pour off the clean liquid into another vessel and apply. The solution must be freshly made and used while still hot. Since it is caustic, care should be taken not to spill it on clothes or immerse the hands for longer than is necessary. Finally, rinse all appliances in clean water.

Prevention of disease being better than cure, try always to observe the following rules :

1 Always keep the apiary clean and tidy, never throw old comb or propolis around. Regularly inspect and clean waste matter not removed by the bees from the floor of the hive.

2 Never buy old combs. Practise a system of systematically renewing combs in the brood box every year, substituting at least two new frames of foundation on the outside of the brood box immediately after the nectar flow at the end of the summer.

3 Only buy colonies of bees from recognized disease-free apiaries. Try never to accept strange swarms of unknown origin.

4 Disinfect second-hand hives before use by the method described above.

5 Do not feed honey from unknown or foreign sources ; feeding sugar syrup, though thought by some to be unnatural, is far safer.

6 If a colony dies during the winter and it is not due to starvation, close the hive to prevent remaining stores being robbed by other bees.

7 Do not exchange brood or super combs between one colony and another unless you are sure that all are free from disease.

8 Arrange hives in such a way that drifting is kept to a minimum.

9 Try to prevent robbing by other bees at all times. The greatest disease spreader is the robber bee. All bees, when nectar is in short supply, attempt to raid other stocks and those least able to defend themselves are sick stock. The robber bee carries home not only the honey but the disease as well and this will explain why the strongest colony in the apiary is often the first to display signs of disease. Prevent robbing by keeping colonies up to their full strength, not spilling syrup and not feeding until the bees have finished flying for the day. Reduce the entrance on hives of weak stocks.

10 Maintain a clean supply of water near the hive to discourage bees drinking from polluted sources.

11 Keep a careful watch for any of the tell-tale signs.

European foulbrood

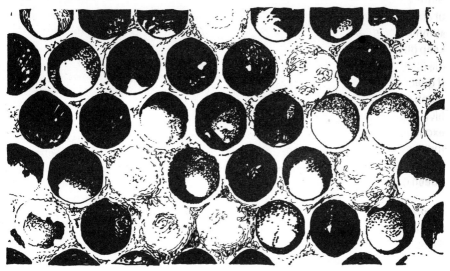

Pests and Other Mishaps

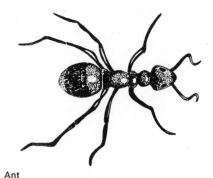

Ant

Diseases of Adult Bees

Acarine : bees crawling near the hive
with misplaced K-shaped wings.
Nosema : inability to fly, decrease in
numbers, excretia in combs.
Amoeba : similar to nosema, usually
a spring disease.
Paralysis : black, shiny bees ejected
from the hive trying to return. Loss
of strength in late spring.

Diseases of Brood

American foulbrood : sunken dark
cappings, often moist and perforated.
European foulbrood : larvae dead in
cells about four days after hatching.
Chalk brood : cappings can look
normal but may be perforated by
bees or removed.
Sac brood : cappings vary, often
removed by bees and can be dark
and moist.

Queenlessness

Signs are drone brood in worker cells
or absence of brood in spring and
summer. A stock without a queen will
keep going through the winter but will
die out in spring as the workers perish.
If queenlessness is suspected, take a
comb containing brood from another
hive, shake off all the bees and
exchange it for an empty comb from
the queenless hive. If the bees are
queenless, they will immediately build
queen cells.

Starvation

Colonies not left with the statutory
13.6kg (30lb) honey in autumn will
die out through lack of food over the
winter. If the spring is late, even
colonies which have been left with an
adequate supply may need some
feeding to carry them through the bad
weather until they can get out to
forage. A spell of rain in summer lasting
more than a couple of weeks will
deplete food stocks in the hive when
breeding is at its height and the colony
will require feeding to maintain its
strength. Indications of starvation are
bees dead in cells, having died during
their last desperate attempt to get food.

Damp

Strong colonies in sound hives can
stand extreme cold, but damp from a
leaking roof, or a floor which is not
tilted at enough of an angle to throw
off water, will leave them dead in piles
on the floor often covered by mould.

Pollution

Most pesticides are lethal to bees.
Those based on derris or pyrethrum are
the least deadly and some sprays are
safe if used in the evening after the
bees have stopped flying. Sprays
should never be used on open blossom
and try to get prior notice from a farmer
when he is about to do large-scale
spraying of field crops such as rape,

Flycatcher

Mouse

lines of black cotton between them.
Mice : in winter, will creep in the hive
entrance if it is large enough, and eat
both comb and honey. A mouse
excluder or the entrance reduced to
two bee spaces will prevent this.
Moths attack stored combs. Wrap
spare combs and supers in newspaper,
put 30g (1oz) paradichlorobenzene
crystals on top and cover with sacking
to keep in the fumes.

Wasp

and shut the bees up for that day.
However, in warm weather remember
to remove the lid and a solid coverboard
and replace with a ventilated
coverboard.

Enemies

Wasps are great hive robbers. Where
there is evidence of their work, restrict
the entrance to one bee space to help
the bees defend their hive.
Ants love honey and will crawl up the
legs and into the hive. Stand the legs
in a tin of paraffin or creosote or wrap
them in oil soaked rags or sacking if
these raids are suspected.
Birds : tits and flycatchers are fond of
eating bees. To prevent this, stick two
bamboo canes at an angle of 45° on
each side of the entrance and then run

Opening the Hive

Hives should not be opened except for a specific purpose, such as : inspection for queen cells in spring (an indication of swarming) ; routine checks for disease and brood rearing (meaning that the queen is present and healthy) ; to see how full of honey the supers are and if more are needed in summer ; and, in autumn, that there is enough honey to last the winter.

Before opening the hive, have ready everything that is necessary for the operation and be sure you know what you are going to do and that you can carry it through without interruption. If you are interrupted, the cover must be replaced over the combs and the roof put back. Brood combs must never be exposed to cold or sun more than can be avoided.

Bees are very susceptible to weather conditions. On thundery, cold or windy days they become very aggressive, rushing out in great numbers to attack and sting. When the weather is warm and sunny with nectar and pollen abundant, they react quite differently and are relatively placid and amenable. Therefore the ideal time to open the hive is the middle of a fine day when large numbers are out foraging.

Bees react badly to nervous, unsteady movements, jarring or loud noises, and they are easily crushed which disturbs the other bees. All this makes it difficult for the beginner. A cloud of what can be in numbers about forty to fifty thousand bees rising with angry buzzes from the open hive is disturbing, to say the least. And the lack of confidence which led to the unsteady movement which instigated the attack will not be helped by having

Opening the hive

to placate these crotchety thousands.

To avoid this, take everything as slowly as possible at first. Puff away with the smoker and try to be as gentle and as smooth as possible with every movement. Being stung is part of the process of learning. Initially, I never managed to open a hive by myself without collecting at least one sting, no matter how carefully I dressed and tried to follow the rules. Expect it and try not to get alarmed when it happens.

Keeping all these factors in mind, with your tools together, properly dressed, and with the smoker working well, approach the hive. Give a couple of good puffs of smoke into the entrance. Wait a minute by the side of the hive for the smoke to take effect. This is to send the bees rushing to their combs and start gorging themselves on honey. A relic of their forest past is that bees fear fire. Smoke raises this prehistoric fear and, thinking that

departure from their present home to find another may be imminent and this will require strength and food, they temporarily forget about defending themselves and become much subdued. The continued use of the smoker keeps the bees subdued. Bees are a bit like wilful children : once they understand that a firm person is in control, they tend, with occasional reminders, to be obedient. After a minute, stand the smoker by the side of the hive within easy reach, and lift off the roof. Put it upside down on one side to enable any bees in the lid to escape, then loosen the coverboard with your hive tool, lift one corner and puff some smoke in the gap. Lean the coverboard against the hive, making sure that no bees are crushed in the process. Then, depending on the time of year and the reason for opening the hive, follow one of the processes on the next page.

Inspecting the Hive

Inspecting the Brood Box

To inspect the brood box, remove the roof and stand it upside down, then take off the coverboard and super together and stand them askew on the lid. Puff some smoke across the excluder to drive the bees down, lever it off, give it a sharp shake over the brood box to rid it of bees, and stand to one side. Then puff a little smoke, if necessary, over the top of the brood box and, starting at one side, loosen the ends of the first frame. Put the hive tool within easy reach and, holding the frame lugs between thumb and forefinger, lift the frame slowly up trying to avoid rubbing the bees against the next frame or the hive wall. Once clear of the hive, lift the frame up and inspect the side nearest you. Combs of any kind should never be held flat. Being heavy with brood or honey, the whole comb could drop out and, in any circumstances, honey drips from uncapped cells.

To turn a frame so that every side is inspected, revolve it in the manner shown in the diagrams, using the top bar as an axis and returning the frame to its original position by reversing the movements. The first comb is not replaced in the hive but given a jerk to deposit the bees back on the top of the brood box and stood on its side against the hive. This leaves more space for manipulating subsequent frames. The second frame is then loosened, picked up, inspected and replaced in the space vacated by the first and so on, until all the frames have been inspected. Frames should always be held over the brood box so that, if the queen is on a

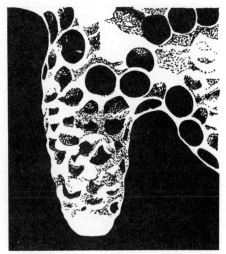

Queen cells

particular frame and happens to fall, she lands back in the brood. At the end, the frames should be moved back into their original positions and the first one replaced. This is very important in order to keep the pattern of the brood box in place. Finally, check and adjust the spacings between each frame and replace the rest of the hive.

When opening a brood box the things to look for are :

1 The presence of the queen. It may be difficult to spot her at first but if there are evenly patterned eggs the odds are she is there.

2 Evidence that she is laying, in which case you will see little white eggs.

3 Capped brood in the centre of the combs and the cells filled with pollen which, depending on the source, can be of all colours, and are situated round the brood cells.

Honey is stored in the topmost corners of the frames, and the drone cells with their distinctive domed caps tend to be placed towards the lower corners of the outermost combs.

In spring, queen cells should be looked for. These are usually situated on the bottom of the frame, though sometimes they can be elsewhere and are often difficult to see if the bees are clustered thickly over them. As the season progresses, the ratio of brood to pollen to honey will change, with the latter taking over from the former.

When the inspection is over, puff some more smoke over the brood box. Replace the queen excluder, then the super, coverboard and roof, making sure they are exactly positioned and straight. To finish, collect tools together and write up any relevant notes or observations.

Inspecting for Honey

To see how full the supers are, remove and inspect each frame as described for the brood box. Since bees are more inclined to fill the middle frames with honey rather than the outer frames, it is a good idea to change the position of the frames in honey supers. Place empty or half-full frames in the middle and move the full middle ones to the outside—something that should never be done in the brood box. If the supers are full, another fitted with the right number of frames of foundation can be added. Since bees are always reluctant to move into empty supers, they should be placed beneath a full one. Loosen the top full super, remove and stand askew on the upturned lid of the hive. Fit on the empty super and place the full one on top. Replace the coverboard and lid, making sure that they are exactly in place.

Cleaning the Floor of the Hive

Once a year in early spring, the brood box itself should be removed and the floor of the hive scraped with the hive tool to remove wax, propolis and other debris.

Turning a frame for inspection

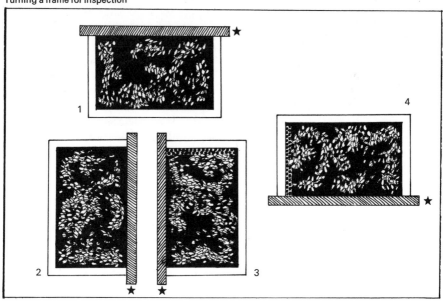

Seasonal Management

Autumn—Late August to October

For the colony to survive the winter, and emerge well enough for them to be able to enlarge their population efficiently in spring, certain precautions must be taken in the autumn.

Queen

Queens that are over two years old are best replaced now (see requeening p 40). Also requeen colonies which have been bad-tempered or otherwise inadequate during the season.

Food

There should be sufficient supplies of food in the combs. A strong colony needs between 16 and 18kg (35 and 40lb) honey to see it through the winter and this amount should be left in the hive when the surplus is taken off in August. If this quantity is not present, sugar syrup must be fed to make up the deficit. The more food that bees have in autumn the better progress they will make in spring and,

consequently, the more honey they will make the following year. Except in heather districts, which provide a late harvest for the bees, feeding should begin in September and be completed as quickly as possible. The colder the weather becomes the sleepier the bees. If they are not given enough time to store and seal the syrup before this, the unripened stores will ferment. Beware of robber bees when feeding. Take the precaution of not feeding before sunset, contracting the entrance of the hive and not spilling syrup about in the apiary. Syrup for autumn feeding should be made in the proportions 4.5kg (10lb) white sugar to 2.8l (5pt) water. Put in a rapid feeder.

Brood Chamber

In late August, if an inspection shows the brood chamber to be so full of honey that there is no room for the queen to lay, remove one middle comb of sealed honey and replace it with a frame of foundation. The removed comb can be replaced later to make up for the honey used. But if the chamber is so full of brood that all the honey is stored in the super, as long as the weather is good, do nothing. Later, however, do be sure that such a stock has enough for the winter, since they may need a full super of honey over the brood chamber to see them through the season.

Mouse-Guard

Mice often fancy the idea of spending the winter in a hive and can do a lot of damage to combs and disturb the bees. Entrances should be protected to prevent this happening. If possible, buy a special perforated mouse-guard; this has holes large enough for the bees to pass through but too small for mice to do so. Place it in position in October. Alternatively, entrances can be curtailed by slipping in two long strips of wood on either side of the entrance until it is closed to about 1.2cm ($\frac{1}{2}$in). This keeps out the mice. However, it

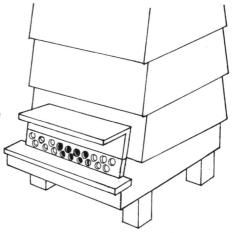

Mouse-guard in position

can also impede ventilation that is so vital in the winter.

Birds

In some areas woodpeckers are a problem. Protect hives by draping them with fruit- or fish-netting or by erecting a barrier of barbed wire.

Making the Hive Wintertight

Remove the queen excluders and the supers. Make sure the hive is thoroughly weatherproof and stable. If the hive is in an exposed position, strong winds may blow it over. To prevent this, weigh down the roof with bricks or stones or even rope the hive to the ground. If hives are in fields full of stock, make sure that the fencing around their enclosure is secure. Roofs should be inspected to see that they are waterproof and check to see that the ventilators are free.

A sound, dry hive with ample food is the best thing you can provide for the bees to help them get safely through the winter.

Netting to protect hive

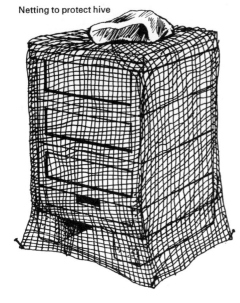

Seasonal Management

Winter—November to March

All autumn preparations should be completed by the end of October. From then until March the bees will not need any attention apart from occasional visits to the apiary to make sure that all is well, that the hives have not been disturbed and that their entrances have not become blocked. This can happen when dead bees fall from the clusters and pile against the mouse-guards. Bees do not fly in winter apart from cleansing flights made on mild, sunny days. During these flights they excrete, a function honeybees never perform in the hive unless suffering from dysentery. For as long as they continue to fly they can survive, even when the temperature is only a few degrees above freezing. However, should they try to alight on the ground or the alighting board of their hive for any length of time, they become chilled and die. The intense light reflected into the hive from snow-covered ground can tempt them out to fly. Since they often land on the snow which kills them, a board should be propped in front of the entrance to shade it when snow is on the ground as this will prevent them from attempting to leave the hive.

Winter is a good time to check equipment, assess the past season and decide on a policy for the coming one. Catalogues of equipment make alluring reading and ordering supplies early is always a good idea.

Most of the bee associations meet

during winter. If you have a local one, go along ; you will be able to make good contacts with other beekeepers and hear informative, interesting lectures as well.

During the winter bees form a cluster in the centre of the hive to maintain the temperature of about 20°C (68°F) that is necessary for their survival. It is this ability of the honeybee (*Apis mellifera*) to cluster which enables it to survive in extremes of temperature from arctic cold to tropical heat and which has made its continued existence possible. The bee is a cold-blooded animal and her body temperature, when resting, approximates to the air around her (when taking exercise her temperature rises). As soon as a bee's body temperature drops below 7.8°C (46°F) she becomes chilled and incapable of movement. It is for this reason that, when the outside temperature drops to about 13.3°C (56°F) usually from about the middle of November to February, although the general atmosphere of the hive is much the same as that outside, the bees form a compact cluster on a small number of combs and in the spaces between to keep themselves warm. The cluster collectively provides considerable thermal protection and the air outside this part of the hive seldom drops below 20°C (68°F) and can rise to as much as 30°C (86°F). The temperature of the bees is maintained by contraction and expansion of the cluster according to the outside temperature. So, with the advent of cold weather when the bees begin to cluster, it is only loosely formed but, as the cold increases, the bees pack themselves tighter together. Sometime after Christmas, usually in early February, brood rearing begins and the temperature of the hive is raised to 32–35°C (90–95°F)—the heat necessary to keep the brood warm and hatching.

Cluster of bees

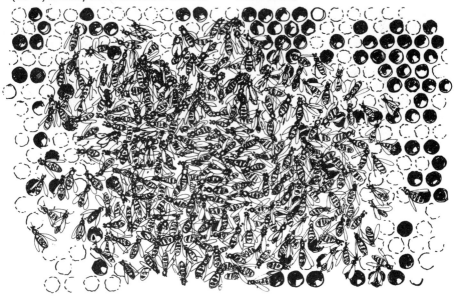

Seasonal Management

Spring—March to May

As the weather becomes finer and warmer in March, the bees begin to fly in stronger numbers and, in the hive, there is a rapid expansion of the brood nest to replace old, outworn bees. If the bees had adequate supplies in autumn, and the spring is reasonably early, feeding will not be necessary at this time. However, if supplies were short or the spring is late, some feeding, about 2.2 l ($\frac{1}{2}$gal) syrup, may be necessary. The experienced will be able to tell if a hive is light by hefting, or gently lifting each hive from the back. If it feels light then stores are needed.

Bees use a great deal of water in spring to dilute the congealed winter honey. To prevent them collecting it from polluted sources, a supply of fresh water should be provided. Choose a warm, protected spot near the hive but out of line of the direct flight-path where it may become contaminated by faeces. A bird-bath, with stones for the bees to rest on, is practical and looks good also. Two jam-jars inverted over a wooden board, scored with grooves so that the water can seep out will be equally efficient.

First Inspection of the Hive

Either in April or when the apple blossom is out and on a fine day will be time enough to make the first inspection of the hive. The things to look for are:

1 That the queen is present and laying —evident from a quick look at the centre combs in the brood box which should contain compact areas of slightly domed, sealed cells surrounded by neatly coiled, pearly white larvae.
2 That the brood is healthy and correct. A scattered brood pattern in worker cells with markedly domed cappings is an indication that the queen is a drone layer or that drone brood is being raised from the eggs of laying workers owing to the loss of the queen. Any colony in this condition should be united with another normal colony.

3 Disease. Check the brood for any signs that might indicate disease such as dark, sunken or perforated cappings, or any of the other symptoms mentioned on pp 20, 22

4 That there are adequate stores to meet the demand of the expanding brood nest.

5 Remove mouse-guards, which are no longer needed.

Second Inspection of the Hive

The second inspection of the hive should be more thorough and made in late April or early May.

1 Clean the frame tops. Propolis and ridges of bee space obscuring comb should be scraped off with the hive tool. Clear the debris and droppings off the floorboard. This is most easily done by having a spare floorboard and substituting it for the dirty one which can then be cleaned and substituted for the dirty one on the next hive, and so on.

2 Replace combs that are mis-shapen or otherwise in bad condition with sound, drawn ones. If frames fitted with foundation have to be used, place them on the edges of the brood box between the frames of drawn comb, ie in position two and ten of an eleven-frame box.

3 Assess the room required for the expanding colony. Colonies with brood on less than six or seven combs do not need extra room at this stage. For those covering seven combs, a shallow super of drawn comb will suffice, but those with brood on eight or more will need another brood box of drawn combs. Put one comb of brood from the bottom chamber in the middle of the new top one. Close up the gap in the bottom chamber and put the new frame of drawn comb on the outside. Doing this will encourage the bees to enter the top brood box.

Uniting Colonies

Two weak colonies may be united by destroying the queen in one, then sprinkling both lots of bees with diluted sugar syrup or flour and interspersing the best combs from both in one box.

Two strong colonies can be united by the newspaper method. Remove the queen from one colony. In the evening, place a double thickness of newspaper pricked with holes over the top of the queen right brood box. Then place the box containing the queenless brood on top of this. The time taken for the bees to chew through the newspaper seems to be enough to acclimatize them to the idea of amicably accepting each other. After a week, the combs can be sorted and rearranged with brood combs in the middle and stores on the outside and, if necessary, one brood box removed.

Newspaper separating queenless brood box (1) from queen right brood box (2)

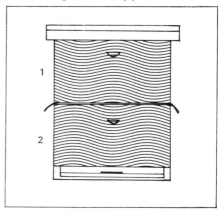

Seasonal Management

Summer—May to August

As a natural course bees build up their numbers on flowers in spring and go through a period of intensive reproduction. If the hive becomes congested during this time, they build queen cells and swarm, and then concentrate on the collection of enough stores to see them through the winter. The beekeeper's object is to encourage the first and last stages of this procedure but to discourage swarming. He does this by providing plenty of space in the brood box for breeding in the spring, inspecting the hives for queen cells every seven to ten days during the crucial swarming period, ie from early May to mid July (see p 36), and by providing space in the form of supers for the storage of the winter's supply of honey.

If, by good management, fine weather and a heavy nectar flow you can achieve a maximum number of foragers, and prevent swarming, then the ingredients are all there for a massive build-up of honey-stores which will be surplus to the bees' winter requirements and which the beekeeper can use himself.

If things go wrong, the beekeeper may find himself feeding the bees sugar syrup during the summer and having no honey in the autumn. Bad management of weak colonies in spring, swarming and prolonged bad weather in summer, during which time

Combs (1) Drawn (2) Filled (3) Capped

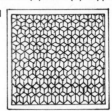

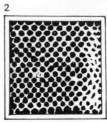

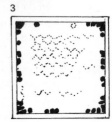

the bees, unable to forage, have to be fed in order to survive, can all contribute.

If, during spring, ample room has been given in the brood box and supplies of food ensured at all times, by the end of May, or when the bees are beginning to occupy the outer frames of the brood box, the first super can be added over a queen excluder. Supers should always be added sooner rather than later to avoid congestion and consequent swarming. Also, when the weather is bad and the bees are kept at home, there will be room and supplies for all. The super should be gently lifted into place, making sure that no bees are crushed in the process and, if possible, should be full of drawn combs. Undrawn combs should be reserved for later in the season when the nectar flow gets under way and the colonies are stronger. Shallow supers are most frequently used, though deep brood boxes can also be used and, indeed, this is a good way of obtaining drawn comb for later use in the brood box itself.

When the bees begin to cover the outer combs of the first super, a second one can be added, with subsequent ones on top of that. The average strong colony will fill three to four shallow supers during the summer, though in a bumper season they will fill several more. At the height of a good nectar flow, bees will bring in 1.8–4.5kg (4–10lb) nectar a day; the average super frame holds 2.2kg (5lb).

Apart from periodic checks to see that the brood box is healthy, bees do not need detailed inspection during the summer. It will be enough to continue adding supers as required.

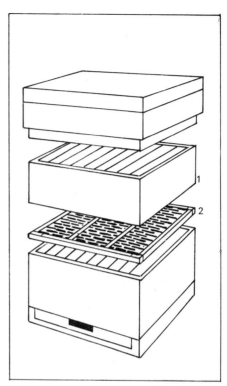

1 Super; 2 Queen excluder

Section Honey

The beginner is advised not to try for section honey unless his colonies are exceptionally strong and there is a good nectar flow. If he wants comb honey, he will be wiser to buy unwired foundation and aim for cut comb. The bees, for some reason, dislike having to climb over the wooden sections and experience in the placing and the number of sections is required in order to be successful. Good sections need to be drawn, filled and capped quickly. They can be bought flat or made up and, to encourage the bees into them, it is a good idea to intersperse layers of section with layers of partly filled comb.

Swarming

Bees, no less than any other species, have to reproduce in order to survive but because bees can only exist in colonies, unlike most other living things, it is the colony itself which must reproduce. It does so by swarming. A swarm consists of an old queen with attendant bees. The hive she leaves will have queen cells containing her successor and enough bees to look after her and forage for food.

Apart from natural disasters beyond human control, such as fire, there are other situations which build up from conditions within the hive which, if corrected in time, can help prevent swarming. Nothing has yet been discovered to prevent swarming altogether. In fact, for many ages, swarming of bees was encouraged by beekeepers as a way of increasing their stocks. It is only since the invention of modern hives and bee maintenance that the study of swarm prevention has begun. Swarming to this extent is still inbred in our bees.

There are many theories as to why bees swarm, dealt with in full in the HMSO Bulletin 206, 'The Swarming of Bees', but the two main causes are thought to be the ageing of the queen and overcrowding in the hive.

At the centre of every bee's existence is the queen and without her presence they die. She makes her presence felt by producing a chemical called queen substance which is licked off her by the bees and somehow distributed throughout the hive. It has been suggested that, as a queen ages, the amount of substance she produces decreases, giving an incentive to the bees to build queen cells for a replacement. Concerning the theory of overcrowding in the hive, towards the end of May the spring blossom has passed its peak and there is a decline in

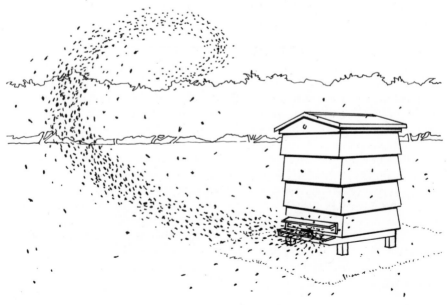

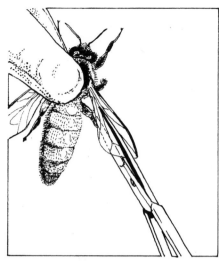

Clipping queen bee's wing

incoming nectar until the summer flush of flowers begins. This period of poor nectar flow coincides with the hive being at its maximum, with many new young bees, in addition to numerous foragers with no foraging to do. It is at this time also, from mid-May to mid-June that prime swarms usually issue.

Unless you actually hope that your bees will swarm as a means of increasing your stocks—though, even so, it will be wiser to take a hand and create a nucleus in case the swarm issues without your seeing it and is lost (see p 38)—certain precautions can be taken to reduce the possibility of swarming to a minimum:

1 Keep a strain of bees not given to excessive swarming.
2 Requeen every two years to ensure a good supply of queen substance and brood.
3 Make sure that there is enough room in the brood box. If there are any signs of overcrowding, add another brood box or shallow super with full complement of drawn combs, replacing the queen excluder over this.
4 Remove the queen cells. This is a lot of work, it entails carefully inspecting every comb in the brood box and destroy any remaining queen cells. The new colony should be left undisturbed for at least three weeks for the new queen to mate and begin laying. clustering thickly around queen cells and obscuring them.
5 Clip the queen's wings. This is done with a pair of fine scissors. Pick the queen up by her thorax and clip the large wing on one side down the middle. Make sure that you do not clip a leg as well—practise on a few drones first. The theory is that any swarm which issues will not travel far, being without a queen, and will return to the hive. A new queen is clipped as soon as the worker brood in the hive indicates that she has been mated. However, there is always a danger that bees will supersede a clipped queen, disliking her deformity.
6 Artificial swarming. When queen cells are in an advanced stage, the colony is divided. Follow the directions for forming a nucleus on p 14.

Collecting a Swarm

No matter what preventive measures are taken, swarms will issue. Nevertheless, heart can be taken from the fact that a bad swarming season is often a good honey season. If you are lucky, either you or a neighbour will be there to see the swarm. If, however, no one sees it, they may be lost for good. A fine, dry day is always chosen for swarming. Ominous signs are the appearance of drones and worker bees not rushing out of the hive as eagerly as usual but tending to cluster near the entrance instead. However, you may just look out of the window to see the air swirling with black dots which, after a while, suddenly take direction and stream towards what you hope will be an accessible low bough, not a hedge or high roof eave. Here they will cluster in a great loose moving mass while the scouts go hither and thither looking for a good new home. At this time they are full of honey and in a good temper. Later, if the scouts are unable to find a suitable home and the honey is used up, they become increasingly irritable. Therefore, the earlier you collect the swarm the better.

A straw skep is traditionally used to collect a swarm but a clean cardboard box will do just as well. Wait until the swarm has thoroughly settled, then, if it is on a bough, hold the skep beneath the swarm and give the bough a good shake to make the bees fall into the skep. If the swarm is in a hedge or thick bush, prop the skep over it and smoke the bees up into it. Swarms in trees or roofs will have to be reached by ladder or the box raised on a pitchfork. If clustered around a solid fence or tree, brush the bees off into the skep.

Having collected the swarm, turn the skep over and lay in a shady place near to where the swarm was collected. Prop up one edge with a stick or stone to allow free access for the bees which, if without the queen, will return to where she is and you will have to start all over again.

Hive the swarm in the evening. Prepare a new hive with a brood box and frames fitted with foundation, preferably with at least two drawn combs. There are two ways of hiving a swarm:

1 Place a piece of plywood or hardboard the width of the hive and slope it from the entrance to the ground leaving no gaps. Cover with a white sheet. Shake the bees from the skep on to the sheet and they should run up and into the hive.

2 Put a floorboard and an empty brood box or shallow super in place. Hold the skep over the brood box and jerk

the bees out into it. Then put the prepared brood chamber on top, cover and leave until the bees have crawled up into it. After this, remove the empty bottom chamber and rebuild the hive. The advantage of this scheme is that the bees can be hived at any time with no danger of their flying off.

Feed all newly hived swarms generously for the first few days and

longer if there is no heavy nectar flow. It is a good idea to place the new hive with the swarm in the exact position of the parent hive, moving this to one side and with the entrance at right angles to the swarm hive. Foraging bees from the parent colony will then return and join the new swarm strengthening this and decreasing the risk of subsequent swarms issuing from the parent colony. This often happens as subsequent queen cells hatch.

Leave the hives in these positions for five or six days, then move the parent hive to a new site. A parent stock so reduced in numbers will generally destroy any remaining queen cells. The new colony should be left undisturbed for at least three weeks for the new queen to mate and begin laying.

Alternatively, if you do not wish to increase your stock, a swarm may be rehived in its old hive. This ensures a good crop of honey, rather than a possible one from two not particularly strong colonies. The procedure for rehiving is to first go through the parent hive removing all queen cells except one. Then find the queen in the swarm, kill her and run the swarm into the parent hive. As long as there is plenty of room in the hive the bees will not swarm again.

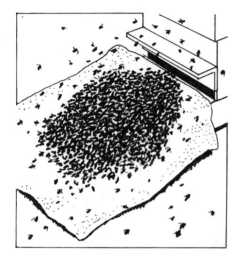

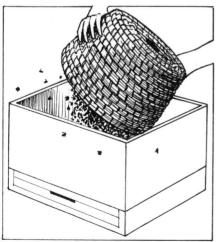

Requeening

Generally speaking, every colony will benefit by being requeened every two seasons. The easiest method for a beginner, or for someone who wishes to improve his existing stock, is to buy a queen of a desirable strain from a reputable breeder. The ideal queen is one without strong swarming tendencies, good tempered, producing disease-free stock and tireless workers prepared to forage in all possible weathers.

The queen will arrive in a wooden box with attendant workers and a store of candy with instructions for her introduction to the hive. Before her introduction to the hive, she must be separated from the workers. This is most easily done by shaking all the

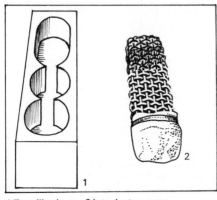

1 Travelling box ; 2 Introductory cage

bees on to a closed window where the queen will show up and can be coaxed into a special introductory cage. These can either be bought from any bee-appliance dealer or made by bending 32mm ($\frac{1}{8}$in) mesh around a plug of wood and covering the other end with newspaper secured with a rubber

band. Having found and destroyed the old queen, suspend the new queen in her cage in the brood box to allow maximum contact with the resident bees. They will release the queen in a few hours by chewing through the newspaper cap.

The experienced and the beekeeper with good stock will want to rear queens of their own. The methods of doing this are legion, but the following is one which is relatively simple. In any apiary with several hives, queen rearing will be found in at least one of them in early summer. In order to make the bees rear the queens and to prevent them swarming, the hive should be rearranged as shown in the diagram and described below. This confines the queen to the lower brood chamber while enabling the workers to continue nursing the queen cells in the upper brood chamber.

To Rearrange a Hive with a Single Brood Chamber

Lift supers and queen excluder and place to one side. Search for the queen in the brood box and, when found, place her and the comb she is on in an empty nucleus box or spare brood chamber, and cover. Lift the parent brood chamber aside and replace with an empty one. Place the comb with the queen in the middle of this and destroy any queen cells on it. Fill up the spaces on either side with empty drawn comb. Put on a queen excluder and supers, and then a modified crownboard on top. The latter is a standard crownboard but with a small entrance gap cut in one side of the raised upper rim and the central feed hole covered, except for an area of about 6.4sq cm (1sq in) over which some zinc queen excluder is secured with the entrance facing the rear of the hive. The original brood chamber with its combs of brood and queen cells is replaced on top. Cover with another crownboard, sufficient supers, a full feeder and the hive roof.

Keep the feeder replenished and otherwise leave the hive undisturbed for five days by which time the queen cells should all be sealed. The queen cells can then be used in three ways :
1 To make one whole new colony.
2 Divided up into nuclei to form several small colonies.
3 To requeen the parent colony.
For the methods for doing the first two see p 42. For the third see below.

Requeening a Parent Colony

Five days after the rearrangement of the combs, ie after the queen cells are sealed but before the queens emerge, the entrance between the modified crownboard and the rest of the hive must be closed, by covering it with thin wood or glass. Leave it like this for about three weeks until the new queen has flown and mated. Keep the feeder replenished with about 550ml (1 pt) syrup a week. At the end of three weeks, if a quick examination shows worker brood, then the two colonies may be reunited. To do this, first find and remove the old queen from the lower brood box. Then cover the lower chamber with a sheet of newspaper, place the top brood with the new queen over the newspaper, cover them in turn with newspaper and put on a queen excluder, the supers, crownboard and the roof. The bees will chew away the newspaper and unite.

Rearranging a hive

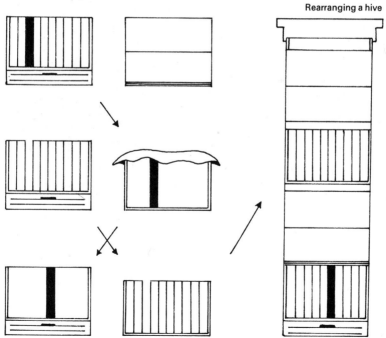

Increasing Stocks

Bees are both expensive and, because of demand, the right kind are frequently difficult to come by. Therefore, the cheapest and most reliable way of increasing the size of an apiary is to make nucleus from good, existing stocks. This may happen naturally by swarming or you can cause it yourself by creating nucleus.

Before beginning, make sure that you have enough empty hives, frames of foundation both drawn and undrawn and supplies of all the other beekeeping paraphernalia in readiness. Only choose that stock for reproduction which has proved itself amenable and good producers of honey. If, when making a nucleus from a hive, you still intend the parent colony to produce surplus honey that season, choose a strong stock and take only one nucelus. If, however, the aim is merely to increase stock, a strong colony can be taken and broken into three or a weak colony broken into two.

At the start, a nucleus should consist of three combs ; one of brood and two well stocked with food. An abundance of food is important, not only for nourishment of the nucelus who may not be able to forage for themselves, but to make them more amenable to the acceptance of a queen or queen cells.

Special nucleus hives can be bought, made either to hold one or two nuclei or several nuclei separated by partitions with separate covers and entrances on opposite ends or sides. One like this can be made from a brood box, divided into four parts, each holding a two-frame nucleus. The advantage of a multiple system is that, while keeping the nucleus separate, it conserves warmth.

If the nucleus is to be given a new queen, introduce her as described on p 40. A nucleus left for twenty-four hours without a queen is usually desperate and will accept one under almost any conditions.

The alternative to buying a new queen is to allow the bees to rear one themselves. There are two ways of doing this : one method produces one new colony, the other produces several nuclei.

For the first method, proceed as described under requeening to the point when the queen cells are sealed. Then remove this brood chamber to a new stand. Reduce the entrance and plug it with grass. When the new queen emerges from one of the cells,

Nucleus of combs

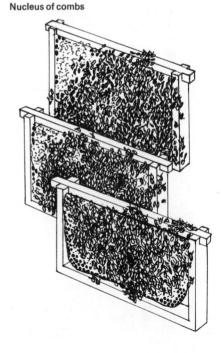

the other queen cells will be destroyed by the bees. Feed the hive with sugar syrup and leave undisturbed for about three weeks. Then inspect to see that the queen is present and laying worker eggs.

For the second method, take three combs well covered with bees : one with sealed brood and a queen cell and two with honey. If there are several queen cells on one frame and none on another, they can be transferred by the following method. Gently brush the bees away from the sealed queen cell. Detach by cutting round with a knife, including a piece of comb extending to 1.2cm ($\frac{1}{2}$in) beyond the cell on all sides. Hold by the surrounding comb and, when ready (queen cells remain sealed for seven days) press into a depression made with your thumb in another comb 5cm (2in) below the top

bar and above a patch of sealed brood. This should be done twenty-four hours after the nucleus has been established, although many people think it better to do it just before the queen cell is due to hatch. This, however, can be difficult for a beginner to judge.

To prevent the bees from the nucleus returning to their old hive, reduce the entrance and plug it with green grass. The bees are unable to get out until the grass has withered and by this time will mark the site of their new hive and return to it.

All nuclei require feeding with sugar syrup until they become established, but the feeding should not begin until three or four days after they have been made up to prevent robbing from other hives.

Transferring queen cells to another frame

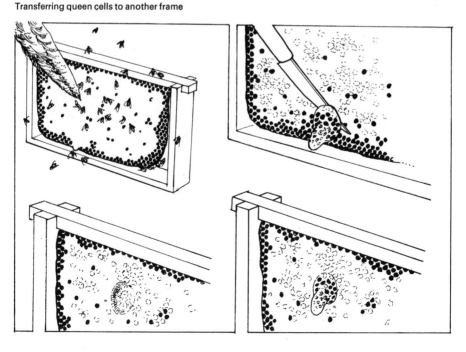

Taking Honey from the Hives

Honey is generally taken from the hives in late August or early September, the time depending on the end of the nectar flow and the exact time a few days before it is over. Working on the premise that bees are pacified by filling themselves up with honey after being frightened by smoke, the longer honey collection is delayed after the nectar flow, the more honey will be sealed and the less there is for them to readily gorge. For the beginner, this will be difficult to judge and more important is the rule that unsealed honey should not be taken from the hive. Bees only seal the caps when the honey has reached a perfect consistency, and the water content reduced to the necessary 20 per cent. Until sealed, honey is not properly ripe. A few uncapped cells do not matter as long as the majority are sealed.

There are two ways of removing supers from the hive. The first is suitable for the novice and the person with only a few hives, while the second is for the experienced person with many hives:

1 On a warm, sunny day, remove the lid from the hive and place it upside down. On this place a clearer board fitted with one or two bee-escapes (these can be bought from any appliance manufacturer), making sure that they are the right way up, ie enabling the bees to pass down into the hive from above. Choosing the side of the super which supports the frame ends, lever up the corner of the super with the hive tool. Puff in a little smoke and raise the super until the frame ends are visible and free. Then lift the super. Since they can weigh as much as 13.6kg (30lb),

First method of removing supers

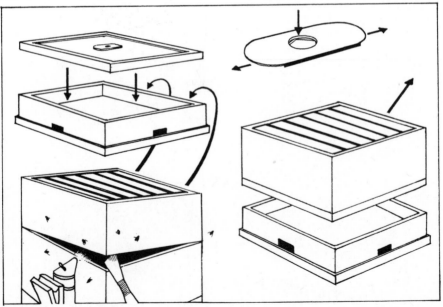

have someone to assist you. Give it a slight twist to free it from the brood chamber and stand it on the clearer. Return the clearer and the super to the hive. If there are two or more supers, the clearer board should be placed under the bottom one. Leave the clearer board in position for several hours or until the next day, chancing to luck that it will be a fine day again. Then take the supers and clearer board immediately to the honey extracting room and seal every entrance to it—the bees will be after their stolen honey.

This is a safe and efficient method of ridding the supers of bees. The only disadvantages are that honey flows more readily when warm and, if the day after putting on the clearer board is not fine and you cannot remove the supers, then honey extraction will be more difficult.

Second method of removing supers

Also, since a clearer board has to be provided for each hive, if there are many hives, the operation becomes a long and drawn out procedure.

2 Take an empty super, two hessian bags and, with hive tool, bee-brush and smoker well alight, approach the first hive. Lay one hessian bag on the ground and place the empty super on top. Remove the roof and inner cover and place these upside down in front of the hive. Puff some smoke into the super and loosen the combs. Take them out one by one, shaking each over the board in front of the hive to remove the bees, then place in the empty super. When all the frames have been transferred in this way, cover them with the other hessian bag. Remove the now empty super from the top of the hive and proceed to the one below, or if there is none, replace the coverboard and roof and proceed to the next hive.

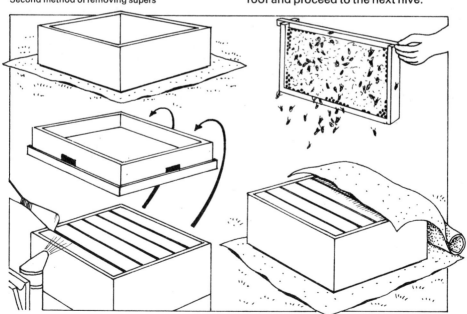

Extracting Honey

The cost of equipment for extracting honey is expensive and, unless the small beekeeper has plans for expansion, it will probably not be worth his while investing the sums required. Some beekeeping associations hire out equipment and sometimes several small beekeepers club together and buy it between them. During your first year you might be able to borrow some, or use a friend's, which will give you an idea of how you want to proceed. The basic equipment consists of :

Extractor: a metal or plastic tank with racks which hold the frames whirled round by turning a handle. The honey is extracted by centrifugal force.

Uncapping

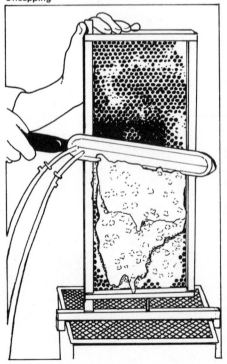

Uncapping tray: this can be a plastic washing-up bowl or tin fitted with mesh across the bottom, to allow honey to drain from the cappings, and with a board resting across the top with a prop or nail hammered upwards the length of a frame lug to hold it steady during uncapping or a heated Pratley tray which separates the wax from the honey.

Uncapping knife: two carving knives stood in jugs of hot water and used alternately ; or a special uncapping knife, or even an electrically heated one. Wipe honey off the blade on to the edge of the uncapping tray before replacing it in the water each time.

Once the frames are removed from the hive, the business of extracting should begin without delay. Therefore make sure all equipment is clean and ready beforehand.

Hold a frame by one lug and rest the other on the support provided by the uncapping tray. Place the hot knife flat against the comb and cut down, slicing off all the caps in one go, allowing them to fall off into the uncapping tray, which they should do in a kind of waxed sheet. Then turn the comb and repeat on the other side. Cut with the end of the knife any parts of the comb which have been avoided because they do not project enough. Put the comb in the extractor, making sure it is fitted right down to the bottom. Only uncap enough combs to fill the extractor. Begin turning the handle, slowly at first, then, as the honey is heard hitting the outside of the extractor, faster. With a radial extractor, continue turning until all the combs are empty. With a tangential one, partially extract the first side, turn the combs and empty the second side, then turn the combs again and finish off the first. This puts less strain on the combs. Replace the empty combs in the super, uncap a second lot and continue until all are done.

As the honey comes up to the level of the cages in the extractor, it should be drawn off into large tins or, if you have one, put it in a settling tank. This has a strainer at the bottom and a tap to draw off the honey. The honey should be left in this for a few days to allow air-bubbles, bits of wax, etc, to rise to the surface before drawing off the honey into tins or jars. If you have no settling tank, put the honey in tins and strain later. Pay attention during straining as honey runs silently and seems to overflow the moment you take your eyes off it. The fineness of the strainer depends on your taste. Some people prefer the odd bit of propolis and comb which comes through a coarse strainer but, for marketing, the clearer the honey the better the average customer will like it. To achieve greater clarity use butter-muslin.

In between all operations keep the honey well covered. If left exposed, it will absorb moisture from the air which gradually causes it to ferment.

After extracting all the honey, replace the empty combs in the super and put back on the hives in the evening. The bees will clean and repair the combs within a few days. Remove them again, wrap in newspaper and store until next year.

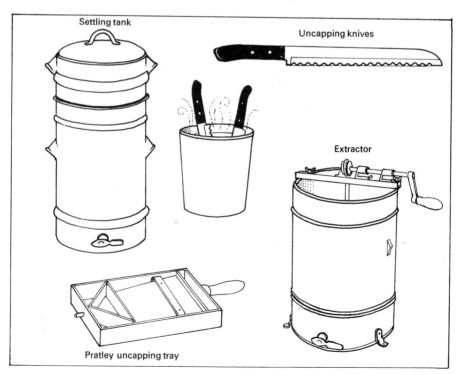

Settling tank

Uncapping knives

Extractor

Pratley uncapping tray

Finishing Honey Production

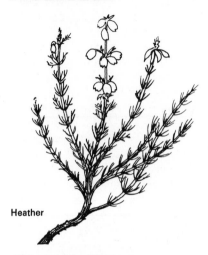

Heather

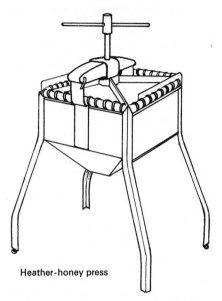

Heather-honey press

Cleaning the Extractor

Close the valve and pour in about 4.5 l (1 gal) warm water, swill it round until it has collected all the wax cappings and honey, then pour into a tin and save it for making mead. Finish cleaning the extractor with hot water and dry thoroughly.

When honey has stopped running out of the cappings, pour these into a container with some warm water and leave them for twenty-four hours. Drain off the water and keep this for mead, put the wax to one side (see p 56).

Extraction of Heather Honey

Due to the relatively high protein content of heather honey which is responsible for its thixotropic properties or jelly-like consistency, it cannot be extracted by centrifugal force but has to be extracted under pressure. The combs are cut from the frames, wrapped in muslin and pressed, usually in special honey presses, until all the honey is forced out and only wax remains. Heather makes perfect section honey. There is usually a heavy nectar flow which the bees gather quickly and seal. It is better collected in sections or used as cut comb rather than extracted honey.

Section Honey

Honey in sections or to be used as cut comb should not be removed from the hive until every cell is full and sealed. Remove the supers or sections in the way described on p 44. Scrape away all propolis and wax and store in airtight tins.

Cut Comb

This avoids the problem of getting the bees to fill sections while enabling you to enjoy honey straight from the comb. Normal frames should be fitted with unwired foundation ; when full and sealed, cut into blocks. For marketing commercially, these should measure about 7 × 9cm (2⅝ × 3½in) each weighing 225g (8oz) and should be put into plastic boxes sold especially for the purpose.

Storing Honey

Honey should be put in its final container as soon after extraction as possible. As already stated, left exposed to the air honey quickly collects moisture, due to its hygroscopic quality, which leads eventually to fermentation. Each time it is poured from one container to another, it loses a little of the precious essences and aroma that go to make up its character. Honey should be stored in airtight containers in an even, dry, atmosphere. A cupboard in the kitchen is ideal.

Liquid, Crystallized and Creamed Honey

Honey is composed mainly of different

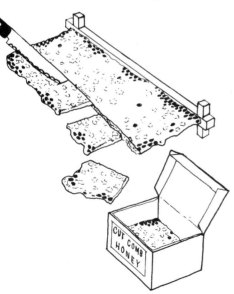

sugars which vary in proportion and quantity with each plant. The rate of granulation of the honey depends on the relative proportions of glucose and fructose in the nectar. Honey with a high glucose/fructose ratio tends to granulate rapidly while honey with a low glucose/fructose ratio granulates slowly. Some honeys, notably acacia, never crystallize, while others, those from charlock and others of the cabbage family, crystallize very quickly. As honey crystallizes, it contracts and sometimes leaves what are called frost marks which show through the side of the jar. These have no effect on the actual taste of the honey.

People who dislike hard crystallized honey often subject it to a process called creaming. The honey is first allowed to granulate in tins, then stood in hot water until liquid enough to be stirred but is never allowed to exceed a temperature of 60°C (140°F). It is then stirred until smooth and creamy and poured into jars. Honey treated in this way remains creamy, though I think it impairs the taste.

Selling Honey

Honey can be sold either in bulk, packed in tins to various firms who then repackage it for retail or in jars through a local shopkeeper, a notice on the gate or even word of mouth. Fill standard 450g (1lb) jars a little above the top ring and, with the cap screwed on lightly, stand in a reasonably warm place for twenty-four hours to allow any scum to rise. Remove this with a spoon and any honey above the ring, screw the caps down tightly and label.

Honey for Cooking

Points to Note when Cooking with Honey

If honey is being used to replace sugar, allow for the fact that it contains 18–20 per cent water and calculate for one fifth less liquid where any is to be added. Honey runs more freely when warm.

Different honeys have different tastes. Mild honeys such as clover or acacia are best for sweetening tea and for light puddings, while stronger honeys can be used for coffee and fruit cakes.

Honey Bread

Mix 120g (8oz) flour with 120g (4oz) sugar. Melt 120g (4oz) honey with 225ml (1 teacup) hot water and add to the flour mixture. Mix well before adding 5ml (1tsp) baking powder or bicarbonate of soda and, if liked, some spices or grated lemon rind. Put into a loaf tin and bake slowly for 1 hour. Serve in thin buttered slices.

Baked Apples with Honey

Core some sound baking apples and fill the centre with honey and one clove. Put in a baking tin and surround with a honey syrup made of 15g (1tbsp) honey to 115ml ($\frac{1}{2}$ cup) hot water. Bake in a moderate oven until the apples are soft.

Honey Pudding

Put 30ml (3dsp) honey in the bottom of a greased pudding basin. Then take 2 eggs and their weight in butter, sugar and self-raising flour. Cream together the butter and sugar, beat in the eggs then fold in the flour. Spoon into pudding basin, cover well and steam for 1$\frac{1}{2}$–2 hours. Serve with more honey or a honey sauce.

Honey Sauce

This can be used for steam puddings or to cover ice-cream, fritters, doughnuts, etc.

Heat together 240g (8oz) honey and 275ml ($\frac{1}{2}$pt) water. Add the rind and juice of 1 lemon or a pinch of ground ginger. Serve hot.

Honey Nut Cookies

Melt 30g (1oz) chocolate with 60g (2oz) margarine or butter. Then add 2 beaten eggs, 120g (4oz) honey, 120g (4oz) sugar, 120g (4oz) plain flour, 60g (2oz) chopped nuts and 3ml ($\frac{1}{2}$tsp) vanilla essence, and mix together well. Then drop in small spoonfuls on a greased tray and bake in a moderate to slow oven. The cookies will still be soft when they emerge from the oven but become crisp as they cool.

Gammon Glazed with Honey

Soak a piece of gammon of about 1.8kg (3$\frac{1}{2}$lb) overnight in cold water. Drain, place skin side down in a large saucepan and cover with fresh, cold water. Bring to the boil and simmer gently for 1$\frac{1}{2}$ hours, topping up with more boiling water whenever the level goes down. Then, if you wish to eat the gammon hot, strip off the skin, score the fat, cover with glaze and bake. But, if you are going to eat it cold, leave the gammon to cool in the liquid and, when cold, strip off the rind, score the fat and place it in a roasting tin.

Glaze

Mix together 30g (2tbsp) liquid honey, 60g (2oz) soft brown sugar and 5g (1tsp) prepared English mustard, and use it to coat the outside of the gammon. Place it in the middle of a hot oven 204°C (400°F) and bake for 15–20 minutes or until golden. Baste frequently.

Honey Glazed Chicken

Cut a chicken into pieces and arrange in a buttered baking dish. Beat together 1 egg, 30ml (2tbsp) oil, soy sauce and lemon or pineapple juice, 15ml (1tbsp) paprika, 55g ($\frac{1}{4}$ cup) liquid honey and 5g (1tsp) salt. Spoon over the chicken pieces and bake in a moderate oven for 1 hour. During cooking, turn and baste the chicken pieces frequently. If necessary, increase oven heat for at least 10 minutes to give a crisp, brown finish.

Honey Drinks

Mead was drunk not only by the ancient British but by all ancient cultures, including the Egyptians, Greeks and Romans. In Nordic areas, before the introduction of wine, mead was the drink for all celebrations including weddings. Indeed, the very word honeymoon is connected with the fact that wedding celebrations lasted for about a month with honey being drunk and eaten, symbolizing the belief that it brought long-life, happiness and fertility.

If, when making mead, certain rules are followed success will be more certain. It is essential to use soft, clean water, rain water or distilled water. Mild honeys such as clover, lime or ling heather are more suitable than strong-tasting honeys. Try to use a wine yeast rather than a common one. Maury is best though Madeira and Malaga also give good results. Sterilize all equipment. Never add chemicals such as cream of tartar to mead. Many recipes advise you to do this and, though it speeds fermentation, it destroys the delicate flavour and aroma of good mead. If possible, make your mead between the end of May and July as, at these times, conditions are most favourable for the propagation and growth of yeast cells. Correspondingly, bottle mead in February when temperatures are at their lowest and fermentation dead. In order for a mead to develop its full character, it is best made in quantity and matured in oak casks for a full seven years. However, for most, this will not be feasible and quite satisfactory mead can be made using glass wine-jars.

The flavour, bouquet and character of mead comes from the floral essences in the honey and the type of yeast used, but the body or oiliness are determined by the proportion of honey to water. The minimum is 900g (2lb) honey to 4.5l (1gal) water and the maximum 2.7kg (6lb) honey to 4.5l (1gal) water. If you use more or less you will not have adequate fermentation. For a dry wine 900g–1.5kg (2–3$\frac{1}{2}$lb) honey are recommended and for a sweet one 1.8–2.7kg (4–6lb). When using honey in water washed from cappings, where the exact proportions are not known, it will be necessary to use a hydrometer to ascertain the honey content. 900g (2lb) will give a specific gravity reading of 1.053; 1.3kg (3lb) 1.075; 1.8kg (4lb) 1.096; and 2.7kg (6lb) 1.128.

Mead

For a general-purpose mead, dissolve 1.3kg (3lb) honey in sufficient water to make 4.5l (1gal) liquid. Bring to the boil and simmer for 3–5 minutes. Leave it until lukewarm, then strain through a double muslin into a fermentation jar and add yeast. Plug the neck of the bottle with cotton-wool and leave it in a warm place with a temperature of 18–21°C (65–70°F) for 2 days. When the first vigorous fermentation has died down, insert an airlock and keep it in a warm place until all fermentation has ceased. This could be 6–8 weeks with a light wine but with a heavy wine fermentation may extend over 6–8 months, with an after-fermentation during the summer of the next two years.

Stand the mead in a cool place, below 15 °C (60 °F) for a month before bottling for the wine to clear. Syphon off into bottles and keep for as long as possible before drinking, at the least for a minimum of 6 months. Store the bottles on their sides in a dry cellar.

Rhodomel

This drink is made with rose-hips. Boil 1.3kg (3lb) rose-hips in 4.5l (1 gal) water for 5 minutes. When cool, mash with your hands or with a wooden spoon and strain through two layers of muslin. Make up to 4.5 l (1 gal) with extra boiled water if necessary. Add 1.8kg (4lb) honey and the juice of 2 lemons. Stir until dissolved and, when lukewarm, add previously activated yeast. Ferment as for mead.

Honey Vinegar

Mixed in equal parts with cider vinegar, 15ml (1 tbsp) drunk every morning keeps one trim and healthy.

Using 900g (2lb) honey to 4.5l (1 gal) water, fill an earthenware or wooden vessel three-quarters full. Add some previously activated yeast, cover it with muslin and leave in an open shed, preferably in the sunshine, for 6–8 weeks. Syphon off into a bottle and keep for a further 2 weeks before using.

Honey Mint Ade

This is a cooling summer drink.

Boil together 90g (6tbsp) chopped mint, 225g (1 teacup) honey and 225ml (1 teacup) water and 115ml ($\frac{1}{2}$ teacup) lemon juice for 10 minutes. Strain, cool and dilute with water to taste.

Honey and Elderberry Syrup

A drink good for colds.

Strip ripe elderberries from their stalks and just cover with water. Boil for 10 minutes, then strain. For every 550ml (1 pt) juice add 170g (6oz) honey and boil again for 5–10 minutes. Skim, bottle, and dilute with water before drinking.

Edinburgh Egg Nog

Separate the yolk and white of an egg and beat the white until stiff. Beat in 5g (1 tsp) honey. Beat together the yolk, a large pinch of ground ginger and cinnamon, 115ml ($\frac{1}{2}$ cup) milk and 15ml (1 tbsp) brandy. Fold in the egg white and serve in a long glass.

Honey for Health and Beauty

Health

The use of honey as a healing substance also has ancient origins. There are references to it being an ingredient in liniments and embrocations in the Bible, the Talmud and the Koran. Mohammed is said to have written that: 'Honey is the remedy for every illness, and the Koran is a remedy for all illnesses of the mind, therefore I recommend you to both remedies, the Koran and honey.' The Egyptians embalmed bodies in honey, Greek athletes were fed honey and, when exhausted, given a honey and water drink. Hippocrates advocated honey for long life and, according to legend, Democritus lived to the age of 109 years with the help of honey. Pliny, too, said that for long life and good health honey should be part of everyone's daily diet. Drink a glass with a mixture of honey and cider vinegar every morning; it clears the system and promotes good health.

Honey as a cure for allergy rashes, skin diseases, burns, infected wounds and even gangrene is well known and authenticated. The following excerpt, which appeared in the December 1955 issue of the *British Bee Journal*, written by Mr Michael Bulman, MD, MS, FRCS, FRCOG, verifies this:

> Some years ago a book (*Honey and Your Health*) came into my possession and from it I learned that 'The external application of honey has an age-old history. The ancient Egyptians used it as a surgical

dressing. The Papyrus Ebers recommended that wounds be covered for four days with linen dipped in honey and incense.' Furthermore, 'During the Middle Ages honey was extensively used in the form of ointments and plasters for boils, wounds, burns and ulcers, plain, or mixed with other ingredients.' Instances of the use of honey as a surgical dressing during recent times, mostly in Continental clinics, are also given.

Having started with a measure of scepticism on my own part and that of my staff, all those who have seen the effects of honey dressings have become convinced of their value . . . When dealing with a large surface it is best to use liquid honey. If granulated honey is supplied it can be liquefied by careful warming. In the liquid condition it can be poured evenly over the surface to be treated or gauze may be soaked in honey and applied so as to cover the surface . . . I have every reason to think that this very simple substance provides one answer to the problem of treatment of many infected wounds. The advantages claimed for it are that it is non-irritating, non-toxic, self-sterile, bactericidal, nutritive, cheap, easily obtained, easily applied and above all, effective.

Coughs and colds are helped and soothed by drinking a mixture of honey and Vitamin C-rich elderberries (see p 53), blackcurrant juice or lemon.

For hypertension and nerves the juice of half a lemon with 15g (1tbsp) honey diluted in warm water is recommended as a daily dose.

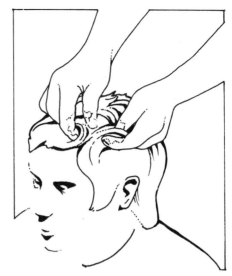

Massaging hair with honey and olive oil

Beauty

Because of its skin-healing properties and its hygroscopical nature (ie it attracts moisture and is easily absorbed by the skin) honey has been used as a beauty treatment by such famous beauties as the Queen of Sheba and Cleopatra, and by the astute ever since.

Actresses whose skin is easily spoiled by the heavy theatrical make-up they have to wear, have been known to alleviate the effects by smearing their faces and necks with honey for 30 minutes each evening. A facial made up of 75g ($\frac{1}{3}$ cup) fine oatmeal mixed with 15g (3tsp) honey or enough to make a smooth paste and 5ml (1tsp) rose-water, if spread over a clean face for 30 minutes, then rinsed off with cold water or astringent lotion, heals any skin problem and promotes beautiful skin, especially if naturally oily.

A treatment to keep hair healthy is to mix 120g (4oz) liquid honey with 60ml (2oz) olive oil. Put in a bottle and store in a dark cupboard. When required, shake the bottle hard and massage a generous amount into the hair for a few minutes. Then wrap the head in hot towels or use a hair-dryer to warm the head and leave the mixture on for 20 minutes before washing off. Do this four to eight times a year. It is especially good for dark hair and it is said that Queen Anne used it on hers.

Bees-wax

Aristotle, Pliny and Columnella all thought that wax was produced from flowers. However, study and science have shown that if, after a household bee has received a load of nectar from a forager, there is no comb space available for its storage so that the bee is forced to hold the nectar in its own honey stomach for hours at a time, a high proportion of the sugar is assimilated, causing the wax glands to secrete wax scales in abundance. Given the space, the bee will begin to build a new comb. The worker bee covers the wax scale with saliva to make it plastic before placing it in position. In this way, irregular masses of wax are built up and subsequently moulded into shape. If, however, there is no space for extra comb in the hive, the bee will drop the transparent pentagonal-shaped wax scales on the floor where they may be found.

Cappings produce the best wax and are also the most consistent source of wax. Other wax comes from scrapings off the hive in the form of burr and brace comb and from old combs.

Wax can be melted down for storage and future use in several ways. Large beekeepers often have an uncapping machine—a sloping tray heated by hot water, steam or electricity. As cappings fall into the tray the honey runs off and the melted wax flows either into a separate container or, more often, in the cheaper kinds, to finish as a wax cake solidified on top of the honey.

Bees-wax can also be melted down in water. The comb should be put in a muslin bag, then in a pan of soft water (rain water ideally but hard water with some vinegar added will do) with a weight on top. As the water heats, the wax floats to the top leaving the impurities in the muslin bag. Left to cool, the wax will solidify into a cake on top. The disadvantage of this method is that the wax can become discoloured with the resins and other substances boiled with it. An alternative is to melt it down by solar heat. A solar extractor can be bought but you can also make one. Leave the extractor out in the open in the sun and occasionally clear away the debris when it is warm. Keep this ; it burns well and can be used as a kind of bees-wax firelighter.

Bees-wax can be used for all manner of things. It is possible to buy metal moulds from which you can make your own foundation. Otherwise bees-wax makes a superlative furniture polish, feeding the wood while producing a subtle shine. All the best lipsticks have a foundation of bees-wax as it is a good emulsifying and colour-carrying agent. Greek sculptors used bees-wax for modelling statues, making deathmasks and wax dolls. Roman athletes rubbed themselves with a mixture of oil, bees-wax and earth before wrestling. Catullus, among others, mentions writing love letters on wax tablets. The Assyrians placed their dead in honey after smearing them with wax, and Herodotus and Strabo wrote that : 'The Persians cover the body with wax after placing it in the ground.'

Bees-wax has always been regarded as the finest material for candles. Although they can be made by dipping wicks in wax then allowing each layer to harden before dipping again, a quicker and easier way is to pour the wax into moulds. Rub a little oil on the walls of the mould first, warm them, then suspend a wick and pour in the wax, doing it slowly to prevent air bubbles from forming. Cool gradually to prevent the candle cracking later.

To make a soothing handcream, melt in a double boiler 130g (4½oz) bees-wax with 180g (6oz) honey and 120g (4oz) lard. Remove from the heat and add 2 drams of bergamot or attar of cloves. Strain and cool.

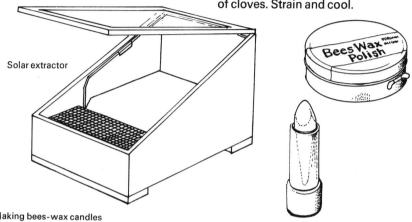

Solar extractor

Making bees-wax candles

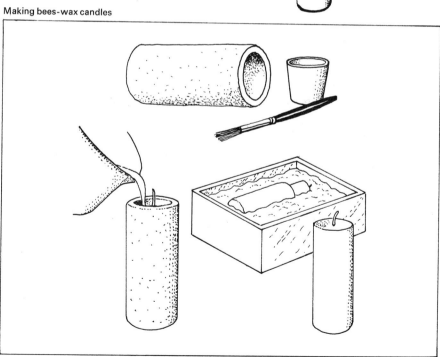

Bee-stings

If you keep bees it is inevitable that at some point you will be stung. No matter how thoroughly you dress in protective clothing, at some time a bee will succeed in getting through and, being flustered, will sting you in defence. However, beekeepers build up an immunity after a time and, apart from feeling a prick as the sting is put in, suffer little or no after-effects. Nevertheless, even experienced beekeepers, after a winter away from the hive, have to rebuild their immunity to some extent. About 2 per cent of people are allergic to bee stings and, in very rare cases, the reaction is so bad that sufferers have been known to collapse and even die. An allergy makes itself apparent by a rash on parts of the body and a feeling of sickness which becomes worse with each sting. The only cure is to give up beekeeping.

While there is nothing that actually cures a bee sting, several remedies soothe the pain. Half an onion, lemon juice, iodine, Dettol, honey are all palliatives and an old remedy is juice of mallow. A cold compress will reduce the swelling. If the sting is obvious, scrape it off with your fingernail but do not attempt to press it out as all you will do is press the poison into your system. In severe cases a doctor should be called and an injection of adrenalin is probably the most effective treatment.

The course of a sting is initial pain at pentration which produces a small red area, soon surrounded by a larger white area and swelling which may be extensive and which will probably irritate. The old idea of a sting being composed of formic acid is wrong. The composition of bee venom is not completely understood, but it is known to be extremely complex and to possess a protein-like toxity.

Rear of worker bee showing position of sting

Barbed sting entering skin

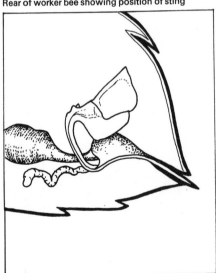
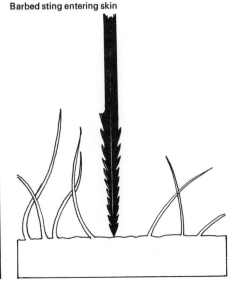

There is an ancient belief that beekeepers never suffer from rheumatism, arthritis or asthma and blindness. While none of these superstitions have ever been proved—and there are beekeepers with rheumatism and all the other complaints—it is a fact that treatment with bee venom has often achieved incredible results. However, until more is known about the chemical composition of bee venom and the various rheumatic complaints, doctors are not prepared to commit themselves. Others are not so particular. Mrs Julia Owen has achieved much publicity recently with her cures for a complaint which leads to blindness, called *Retinitis pigmentosa*. She feeds her bees a special food, which consists partially of the drug which in ordinary medicine would be used to cure the patient, before placing the bees on various parts of the neck to sting.

A bee's sting is hidden inside a cavity at the tip of the abdomen from which it can be quickly protruded when necessary. A bee stings in defence or when frightened, or molested. Beginners are apt to crush bees between hive parts and the smell of this incites the bees to anger as does the smell released by venom after a bee has stung. After stinging a human, the worker bee, in the majority of cases, is unable to withdraw her sting from the flesh and, in the struggle to do so, ruptures the delicate tissue with which it is attached to her body. She breaks away leaving sting and associated structures. Damaged in this way, she may survive a few days but no longer.

Urban Beekeeping

Beekeeping in towns and suburban areas is on the increase. Most people keep from two to three hives, and place them in gardens and allotments, or carry them up to balconies, flat roofs and even put them in lofts and attics with a window left open to provide outside access for the bees. WBC designed hives are the most popular among urban beekeepers, being the most attractive to look at, an important factor especially in a small garden where the hive is constantly on view. National and Commercial hives are also used a great deal.

Honey yields in towns, and in London in particular, exceed anything in the country. There are fewer insecticide sprays to contend with and the average daily temperature is higher than in the country, nor does it drop as low at night. In fact, honey yields decrease the further away from the centre of the town you go. Amounts of honey from 45kg (100lb) to 68kg (150lb) from one hive are not uncommon and, in 1976, a man in Holland Park collected 363kg (800lb) from four hives.

Nectar sources are plentiful. There are more trees per acre in London than in most country areas, lining streets, in squares, parks and gardens. Limes are the most important tree source of nectar, though chestnut, maple and ivy contribute as do many of the more exotic species such as tree of heaven and the tulip tree. The only tree which provides nothing is the London plane. The prodigious numbers of intensively cultivated small gardens in suburban areas are another rich source of nectar. However, there are certain considerations that must be taken into account when keeping bees in built-up, heavily populated areas :

1 Situate your hive so that the flight-path does not interfere with any human passage. If it is likely to do so, then place it with a hedge or fence in front (see p 4).

2 Inform any close neighbours who might become worried or upset at the

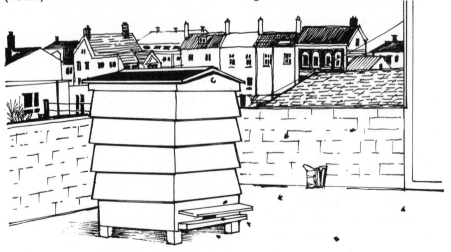

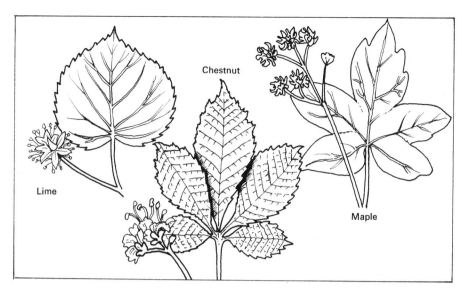

Chestnut

Lime

Maple

thought of having bees so close that the bees' flight-path is straight, will be above their heads and that bees do not hang around close to their hives. After a few months, when they realize that the bees will not disrupt their lives, and a present of honey, they will settle down and forget any thought of menace from your hives.

3 Obtain your bees from docile and preferably local stock adapted to urban living. Your nearest bee association should be able to put you in touch with a source. Most towns have one, and there are several in London.

4 Swarming is the major problem of keeping bees in over-populated areas. If you are not there to see them issue from the hive, the bees will be away out of sight and lost to you. There is also the risk that they may settle, as happened last year, in the cab of a bus in the King's Road or in a lady's bicycle basket parked outside a shop. Alternatively, they may find themselves a more suitable home. Several colonies live in hollow trees on Hampstead Heath and one colony has lived for eight years in an airvent three storeys up a building in Hendon. The police keep lists of beekeepers who can be called in to help with a swarm if necessary, although they say that calls for help with bumble-bee nests outnumber calls to deal with swarms by twenty to one.

5 Open your hive at a time when there are as few people about as possible, preferably in the middle of the day. Another great advantage is to have had previous experience in handling bees. Amateurs who might make a muddle and excite the bees can cause trouble with neighbours which more professional handlers will avoid. Therefore, practical experience obtained through attending a day or evening course is more vital for the urban than the country beginner.

Folklore of Bees

The myths attached to bees and honey are numerous, and no culture which has kept bees is without them. There is only space here to mention a few.

In Greek mythology it was thought that the gifts of speech, poetry and eloquence were conferred on men by The Muses sending bees to touch their lips. Plato, Virgil and Socrates are all said to have had their lips touched by honey when they were infants.

Among the Hindus, in India, honey is a symbol of marriage and fertility. Honey and curds are given to the bridegroom when he first enters his bride's home and, during the wedding ceremony, he kisses her and recites : 'Honey, this is honey, the speech of thy tongue is honey : in my mouth lives the honey of the bee, in my teeth lives peace.' The Brahmans of Bengal used to anoint the bride's forehead, lips, eyelids and ear-lobes with honey to ward off evil spirits and ensure a happy marriage. In the Far East in ancient times the bride was anointed with honey on her breasts and private parts to ensure her fertility.

In Nordic races the belief existed that the souls of men left their bodies in the form of bees. This probably was the origin of the ancient custom of 'telling the bees'. Until quite recently in rural areas it was the habit to tell the bees whenever a person in the family died, particularly if this was the owner of the hive. If this custom was neglected it was thought that the bees would die. The ritual took different forms but, as a rule, the widow or family went to the hive, rapped three times on the side and recited :

Bees, bees, thy master is dead,
Fly not away but remain to comfort me.

In many areas, telling the bees was not only confined to death. All important events were told to the hives in the belief that this made sure they were fruitful. In parts of Germany and Austria it was the custom to dress the hives or bee-house with red cloth during wedding festivals—no doubt another link with the myth that bees were thought of as fertility symbols.

In Lincolnshire a superstition persisted that, if a swarm of bees gathered on the dead bough of a living tree, there would be a death in the beekeeper's family within a year, while in Anglesey they believed that wherever the swarm alighted, that part of the tree would die. The Welsh thought that good luck and prosperity would follow if a foreign swarm entered a garden or house. Buying bees was thought to bring bad luck and so it was customary to barter hives.

In many parts of Europe it was thought that the bees sang a carol on Christmas Eve and it was common for either one member of the household or a procession to visit the apiaries and listen to the bees buzzing their Christmas anthem. On Good Friday in France, palm crosses were attached to the front of the hives to bring prosperity in the coming year and in Cornwall it was maintained that you should only take honey from the hives on 24 August, the day of St Bartholomew, the patron saint of bees.

Another ancient custom was that of 'tanging' the bees or beating on an iron pot with a stick or key, thought to make swarming bees settle quickly. Its original purpose was to indicate ownership of the swarm. Under Roman law bees that had left their hive were classified as *ferae naturae* or wild creatures and, as such, could become the property of anyone who caught them. Consequently, when a beekeeper saw his bees leave the hive in a swarm, he grabbed the nearest object and began banging loudly while running in chase of the swarm. Another custom was to cross oneself and throw a fine shower of dry earth over a swarm to make them settle quickly. This frequently achieved its object, but not through the will of God ; rather the bees believed that it was raining and settled close at hand or even rushed back to the hive.

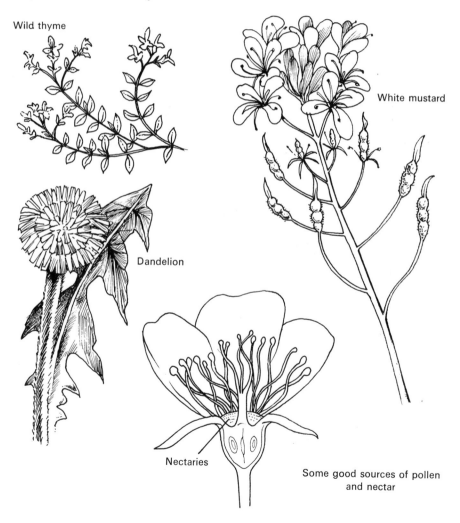

Wild thyme

White mustard

Dandelion

Nectaries

Some good sources of pollen and nectar

Bibliography and Useful Addresses

Beekeeping, Bulletin 9 (HMSO)

Butler, Colin G. *The World of the Honeybee* (Collins, 1975)

Crane, Eva (ed). *Honey* (Heinemann, 1975)

Diseases of Bees, Bulletin 100 (HMSO)

Fraser, H. Malcolm. *Beekeeping in Antiquity* (University of London Press, 1931)

Frisch, Karl von. *Bees, Their Vision, Chemical Senses and Language* (Cape, 1968)

Hodges, Dorothy. *Pollen Loads of the Honeybee* (Bee Research Assn, 1974)

Mace, Herbert. *The Complete Handbook of Beekeeping* (Ward Lock, 1976)

More, Daphne. *Discovering Beekeeping* (Shire, 1977)

Swarming of Bees, Bulletin 206 (HMSO)

Tonsley, Cecil. *Honey for Health* (Tandem, 1973)

Vernon, Frank. *Beekeeping* (Teach Yourself Books, 1976)

Magazines

British Bee Journal, 46 Queen Street, Geddington, Kettering, Northamptonshire

Bee Craft, The Secretary, 21 West Way, Copthorne Bank, Crawley, West Sussex

Bee World (see below, The International Bee Research Association)

Appliance Manufacturers

Robert Lee Ltd, Beehive Works, George Street, Uxbridge, Middlesex

E. H. Taylor Ltd, Beehive Works, Welwyn, Hertfordshire

E. H. Thorne Ltd, Beehive Works, Wragby, Lincolnshire

Associations

The British Beekeeper's Association, General Secretary, 55 Chipstead Lane, Riverhead, Sevenoaks, Kent

The International Bee Research Association, Secretary, IBRA Hill House, Gerrards Cross, Buckinghamshire

British Library Cataloguing in Publication Data

Urquhart, Judy
  Keeping honeybees.—(Penny pinchers).
  1. Bee culture
  I. Title II. Series
  638'.1   SF525

  ISBN 0–7153–7548–2

Set in Univers
and printed in Great Britain
by Redwood Burn Limited
for David & Charles (Publishers) Limited
Brunel House Newton Abbot Devon

Published in the United States of America
by David & Charles Inc
North Pomfret Vermont 05053 USA

Published in Canada
by Douglas David & Charles Limited
1875 Welch Street North Vancouver BC